PATHWAYS

❖

NUMBER ONE

Crossing the Bridge

Gerry Leversha

The United Kingdom Mathematics Trust

Crossing the Bridge

© 2008 United Kingdom Mathematics Trust

Published by The United Kingdom Mathematics Trust.

Maths Challenges Office, School of Mathematics, University of Leeds, Leeds, LS2 9JT, United Kingdom

http://www.ukmt.org.uk

First published 2008.
Reprinted 2011, 2014.

ISBN 978-1-906001-06-3

Printed in the UK for the UKMT by Charlesworth Press, Wakefield.

http://www.charlesworth.com

Typographic design by Andrew Jobbings of Arbelos.

http://www.arbelos.co.uk

Typeset with LaTeX.

The books published by the United Kingdom Mathematics Trust are grouped into series.

❖

The EXCURSIONS IN MATHEMATICS series consists of monographs which focus on a particular topic of interest and investigate it in some detail, using a wide range of ideas and techniques. They are aimed at high school students, undergraduates and others who are prepared to pursue a subject in some depth, but do not require specialised knowledge.

1. *The Backbone of Pascal's Triangle*, Martin Griffiths

2. *A Prime Puzzle*, Martin Griffiths

❖

The HANDBOOKS series is aimed particularly at students at secondary school who are interested in acquiring the knowledge and skills which are useful for tackling challenging problems, such as those posed in the competitions administered by the UKMT and similar organisations.

1. *Plane Euclidean Geometry: Theory and Problems*, A D Gardiner and C J Bradley

2. *Introduction to Inequalities*, C J Bradley

3. *A Mathematical Olympiad Primer*, Geoff C Smith

4. *Introduction to Number Theory*, C J Bradley

5. *A Problem Solver's Handbook*, Andrew Jobbings

❖

The PATHWAYS series aims to provide classroom teaching material for use in secondary schools. Each title develops a subject in more depth and in more detail than is normally required by public examinations or national curricula.

1. *Crossing the Bridge*, Gerry Leversha

2. *The Geometry of the Triangle*, Gerry Leversha

The PROBLEMS series consists of collections of high-quality and original problems of Olympiad standard.

1. *New Problems in Euclidean Geometry*, David Monk

The YEARBOOKS series documents all the UKMT activities, including details of all the challenge papers and solutions, lists of high scorers, accounts of the IMO and Olympiad training camps, and other information about the Trust's work during each year.

Contents

Series Editor's Foreword

This book is part of a series whose aim is to provide classroom teaching material for use in secondary schools. Each title will try to develop a subject in more depth and in more detail than is normally required by public examinations or national curricula. Particular attention is paid to sound pedagogical principles, such as the need for logical clarity in arguments, the importance of learning to tackle multi-stage problems and the recognition of connections between different parts of the subject. The bulk of the text is devoted to carefully constructed exercises, either for classroom discussion or for individual study.

I hope that every secondary school will have these books in its library. The prices have been set so low that many good students will wish to purchase their own copies. Schools wishing to give out large numbers of copies of these books as prizes should note that discounts may be negotiated with the UKMT office.

London, UK   GERRY LEVERSHA

About the author

Gerry Leversha has taught mathematics in secondary schools for over thirty years and has also been involved in the work of the UKMT, both in the setting and marking of various Olympiads and as Chair of the Publications Committee. He is also the editor of *The Mathematical Gazette*, the journal of the Mathematical Association, and is a regular speaker at conferences and summer schools. His interests include music, film and literature, wine and cooking, as well as playing tennis and mountain walking, and his current ambition is to complete the ascent of all 284 Munros in the Scottish Highlands.

Preface

If you wanted to highlight the difference between the kind of mathematical education experienced by a British school pupil in, say, the 1960s and by their contemporary counterpart, you could do little better than look at the way in which geometry is taught. A GCE paper from forty years ago would, not surprisingly, be unrecognisable to today's students. There would, of course, be a high proportion of exercises devoted to algorithmic techniques in arithmetic, made more mysterious by the extensive use of imperial units and pre-decimal currency. This feature has, understandably, been missing ever since the rise of electronic calculators and the internationalisation of everyday life, and few would mourn its passing. Algebra would be similar, although the manipulative requirements of the old paper might be more demanding. There would be no data handling and (unless part of the School Mathematics Project) no probability. The questions, without any pictures, would take up less space on the printed page and there would be fewer hints, so that the general 'look' of the papers would be quite dissimilar. It is, however, the treatment of geometry which would distinguish, in a radical way, the content of the syllabus and the style of teaching. The very title of the discipline has changed, its place in the curriculum being designated as 'shape and space'. Is this new nomenclature a sign that the subject itself has undergone a fundamental change of meaning?

This is not the place to summarise the changes in the perception of school geometry over the last forty years, but many teachers will remember the attempt in the sixties and seventies by the SMP to adopt abstract algebraic methods by rethinking the subject in transformational terms. The backlash against this project and the desire to reintroduce features of the classical approach is the story of the last twenty-five years. This attempt at regeneration was, however, undertaken in a reactive, piecemeal fashion, and the result, unfortunately, is that many essential aspects of geometry are still missing from the subject which is taught today in UK schools. It is the purpose of this book to provide a course for use in the classroom which re-emphasises some traditional features of geometrical education which have disappeared in this process.

Several fundamental aspects of geometry are missing in the contemporary approach. This book emphasises three characteristics which should appear at centre stage, but are either omitted or devalued. These are

- the need for precision in definitions;
- the deductive framework of the discipline and the process of proof;
- the concept of generality.

Why are definitions important? To understand this, one must think about the way in which children come to an appreciation of 'shape and space'. In years 5 to 8 (in the English school system), the approach might be described as 'natural history'. One gains a familiarity with geometrical figures by developing a list of their properties. A square, for instance, has four equal sides, parallel in pairs, with four right-angles at the corners. The diagonals are equal and bisect one another, also at right-angles, and they bisect the angles at the vertices. You know you have a square when you can see all of these properties at the same time. The identification of geometrical objects is therefore analogous to the recognition of, say, liquids or mammals or poems.

This is a valuable and essential part of teaching at a primary school level, but it must, at some stage, be replaced by something else. This is the development of a set of rigorous definitions which allow geometrical objects to be placed in a hierarchy. A square, for instance, might be defined as a parallelogram with a right-angle and with two adjacent sides equal. This, in turn, means that it is both a rectangle and a rhombus. These, in their turn, are both types of parallelogram. A rhombus is also a type of kite. One reason for establishing this hierarchy is that one can be sure that a square has all the properties of a rectangle, and a rectangle all those of a parallelogram, and so on. But the principal reason for insisting on careful definition is that it allows one to have precise rules to deciding what one is talking about.

If a square is defined in terms of all of its properties, then, in order to be sure that something in a figure is a square, one would need to check all of them. It is worthwhile considering an example from the seventies, where a parallelogram was defined as what one obtains by taking a triangle, rotating it through a half-turn about the midpoint of a side, and combining the original figure with its image. This definition has the advantage that all of the symmetrical properties of the parallelogram follow almost at once. But one has to pay for this profligacy, since one now needs to show that any putative parallelogram is the result of the transformation described. It is not enough to observe that there are two pairs of parallel sides. In fact this subtlety was ignored in classrooms, and the result was a devaluation of logic and rigour. In this book, great care is taken over defining geometrical objects properly, and a glossary of these definitions can be found on page 143.

Euclidean geometry certainly used to be viewed — at least in schools — as the prototype of a rigorously deductive system. To some extent, this was a myth, as is evident from the development of much of nineteenth and twentieth century mathematics. However, it was a convenient myth, and it served the purpose of conveying, to generations of school students, an ideal of logical structure and formal development. Classic textbooks took great pains to present a series of definitions, constructions and theorems which built up the subject so that each new result relied upon those which went before. This has now been entirely lost to school mathematics. It could, of course, be argued that there are other ways to teach rigour and to demonstrate the development of mathematics as a formal system — for instance, the introduction of group theory through axioms in a Further Mathematics syllabus. The trouble with that strategy is, of course, that it only exposes pupils to the concept of rigour once they have made a substantial commitment to mathematics. Why should younger students, with some ability at the subject but by no means any desire to specialise in it, be denied access to this important intellectual experience? In this book, therefore, there is an attempt to present the deductive structure of the subject at an earlier stage in the school curriculum.

However, this treatment is, unapologetically, a compromise. It does not begin with explicit axioms, and Euclid's fifth postulate is introduced in a simpler (but equivalent) form as the equality of corresponding angles. There is no discussion of alternatives, such as Playfair's axiom, nor of the Hilbert critique of the Euclidean framework and the consequent introduction of between-ness axioms. Constructions using straight-edge and compasses are left to a fairly late stage in the exposition, and there is no insistence that the compasses can only be used in the strict Euclidean fashion. However, this point is discussed in Chapter 8 and it is shown that one can 'transfer' a distance; once one has this result, one can 'call it' rather like a sub-procedure in programming. The properties of parallel lines, and consequently the angle sum of a triangle, are encountered before congruence, thus enabling AAS to be treated as ASA. It is, of course, possible to introduce the congruence conditions one by one, showing that each can be deduced from the others, but this is not insisted upon and they are met at the same time. This has the advantage that the *pons asinorum* can be discussed in the light of all the congruence conditions together, with, I hope, a clear didactic benefit.

In practice, the treatment at school level has always been a compromise. The trouble is that, if one is insisting on complete rigour, the development of the subject would take so long and be so mentally exhausting that few would make it to the end of the course. Besides, it is necessary to motivate the process by permitting progress to be made, reasonably quickly, to some interesting and unexpected results. It can be very dispiriting to spend all ones time proving the obvious. In the account that follows, various liberties are taken which will annoy the purist. Fundamentalists who disagree with this philosophy can, of course, construct their own course. In the meantime, the intention in this book is that students understand exactly what they are allowed to assume at any stage, particularly in terms of the arsenal of weapons (the theorems) which they are permitted to use. As part of this, the distinction between a theorem and its converse is stressed.

Next, there is the question of generality. School geometry is almost entirely concerned with the particular. A standard question at GCSE starts with a configuration with marked angles and asks the candidate to calculate other angles, possibly 'giving reasons'. Apart from the fact that this provokes the response 'Who cares?', the result of this is that students remain blissfully unaware that geometry is actually about the general — these three points are always collinear, these two lines are always perpendicular, these two angles are always equal. It is worth thinking about an analogy from arithmetic. Consider the following equations:

$$2^2 + 3^2 + 6^2 = 7^2$$
$$3^2 + 4^2 + 12^2 = 13^2$$
$$4^2 + 5^2 + 20^2 = 21^2.$$

Are these simply flukes or is something happening here? What is 'the next equation in the sequence'? What is the general pattern? Can this be expressed in algebraic terms? Can this relationship

$$n^2 + (n+1)^2 + [n(n+1)]^2 = [n(n+1)+1]^2$$

itself be explained in terms of some more fundamental identity? This double process, of seeking a general form and then situating that as an extension of familiar knowledge, is essential to the growth of mathematical understanding. That is why the exercises which have been chosen in this book are not of the GCSE type; although they may be based on a particular configuration, they seek to elicit what is of universal value from it .

Throughout the book, there is an emphasis on proof. Virtually every exercise requires the construction of a careful argument (even if there is no requirement to set it out formally in the time-honoured way). Many of the theorems in the text are set as exercises for the reader, and other examples require the reader to identify bogus 'proofs'.

I hope that this little book will turn out to be a valuable resource.

London, UK   GERRY LEVERSHA

A note on the exercises

The range of difficulty of the exercises is deliberately very wide. Hints are given to some of the more challenging problems. This is, however, not intended as a self-study guide, although for an enthusiastic student it might be usable as such. It is meant to be used in the classroom under the guidance of a teacher who is sympathetic to its aims. There is ample opportunity for whole class discussion of alternative methods and generalisations of the ideas presented.

Certain conventions are observed:

- Polygons are labelled anticlockwise in order of the letters which is often alphabetical;
- $\triangle ABC$ is a triangle, with vertices A, B and C;
- Angles are usually denoted by $\angle ABC$, but, where there is no ambiguity, $\angle B$ is used as an alternative and B is used in trigonometry;
- The area of polygon $PQR \dots S$ is denoted by $[PQR \dots S]$;
- Units are omitted in questions relating to lengths or areas;
- I have decided not to emphasize the distinction between a line, a ray and a line segment.

The first few problems in a group are usually devoted to proving the results which have just been presented. I consider this to be valuable as it emphasises the logical structure of the subject. Again these could be adapted for use in a teaching environment. The content and exercises of Chapters 11, 12 and 13 are at a level of difficulty higher than that of the preceding chapters.

A large number of the problems come from the UKMT challenges and Olympiads, and the sources of these are listed in an appendix. Many of the others relate to quite well-known configurations and can be found in standard geometry texts, written by such masters of exposition as Edwin

Maxwell and Clement Durell. I am very much in their debt. The exercises have been trialled by being presented to school classes at pre-GCSE level. However, I am responsible for any mistakes.

Chapter 1

Angles

1.1 Basic angle facts

Angles on a straight line

If ACB is a straight line, then
$a + b = 180°$.

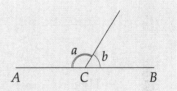

If $a + b = 180°$, then ACB is a straight
line.

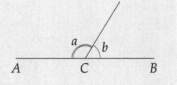

Here there is a result and its *converse*. The first result says

$$\text{If P then Q}$$

and the second result says

$$\text{If Q then P.}$$

It is important to understand which of the two results is being used in any particular situation. Strictly speaking, this should always be specified, but in practice this detail is often omitted, so long as the reasoning is perfectly clear from the context.

Angles at a point

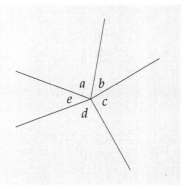

If any number of angles is arranged around a point, their sum is 360°.

In the example shown,
$a + b + c + d + e = 360°$.

Vertically opposite angles

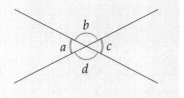

If two lines intersect, then $a = c$ and $b = d$.

Both the above results follow immediately from angles on a straight line.

Problems 1a

1. (a) Show how the result about angles at a point follows from that about angles on a straight line.

    (b) Show how the result about vertically opposite angles follows from that about angles on a straight line.

(c) Is there a converse to the result about angles at a point?

(d) Assuming the result that, if ACB is a straight line, then $a + b = 180°$, prove the converse result.

2. Two straight lines AB and CD meet at the point O. The internal bisectors of angles $\angle AOC$, $\angle AOD$ and $\angle DOB$ are OX, OY and OZ respectively.

   (a) Prove that $\angle XOY$ is a right angle.

   (b) Prove that $\angle COX$ and $\angle DOY$ are complementary.

   (c) Prove that $\angle COX$ and $\angle AOZ$ are supplementary.

   (d) Prove that the points X, O and Z are collinear.

3. Three straight lines OA, OB and OC are drawn from a point O. The line OP bisects $\angle BOA$ and OQ bisects $\angle COB$.

   (a) Show that $\angle POQ = \frac{1}{2}\angle AOC$, where both angles are taken to include the line OB.

   (b) Show that, if $\angle POQ = 90°$, then A, O and C are collinear.

4. (a) If $a = d$ and $b = c$, does it follow that AXC is a straight line?

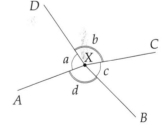

   (b) If $a = d$ and $b = c$, does it follow that BXD is a straight line?

   (c) If $a = c$ and $b = d$, does it follow that AXC is a straight line?

   In each case, if the result is true, prove it, and if it is false, give a counterexample.

1.2   Parallel lines

Corresponding angles

(a) If AB is parallel to CD, then $a = b$.

(b) If $a = b$, then AB is parallel to CD.

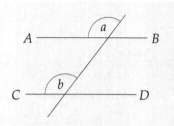

This theorem and converse follow easily from alternate angles.

Alternate angles

(a) If AB is parallel to CD, then $a = b$.

(b) If $a = b$, then AB is parallel to CD.

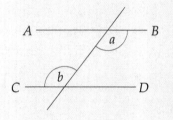

Note that again there is a theorem here as well as its converse.

Included angles

(a) If AB is parallel to CD, then $a + b = 180°$.

(b) If $a + b = 180°$, then AB is parallel to CD.

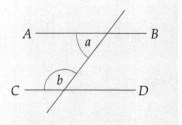

Again the theorem and converse follow from alternate angles.

Problems 1b

1. Use the theorems about corresponding angles to prove those about alternate and included angles and also the converses.

2. Two lines are both parallel to the same line. Prove that they are parallel to each other.

3. Two lines are both perpendicular to the same line. Prove that they are parallel to each other.

4. Prove that the opposite angles of a parallelogram are equal.

5. One of the angles of a parallelogram is a right angle. Prove that the other three angles are also right angles.

6. If PQ is parallel to RS, prove that

$$b + c = 180° + a.$$

With the same diagram, state the converse to this result. If the converse is true, prove it, and if not, say why it is false.

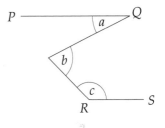

1.3   Triangles and polygons

Angle sum of a polygon

The sum of the angles in a polygon with n sides is $(n-2)180°$.

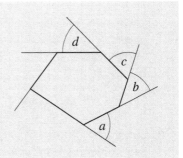

One way to prove this is to consider the external angles, which are marked a, b, c, d, ... in the diagram. Imagine facing to the right at the bottom of the diagram, and then turning anticlockwise through each of these angles in turn. Eventually you will finish facing directly right again. By this time, you will have turned through 360°, so the sum of the external angles is 360°. However, each internal angle is on a straight line with the corresponding external angle, and now a simple piece of algebra yields the result.

(In some books, the words *interior* and *exterior* angles are used instead of internal and external.)

By taking $n = 3$, we obtain the result for a triangle that **the angle sum of a triangle is 180°**. However, it is often very useful to be able to state the closely related result.

External angle of a triangle

The external angle of a triangle is equal to the sum of the opposite internal angles:

$$c = a + b.$$

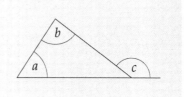

Problems 1c

1. Complete the arguments for the angle sum of a polygon and a triangle.

2. Through the vertex A of $\triangle ABC$, draw a line parallel to BC. Use the properties of parallel lines to prove that the angle sum of a triangle is 180°.

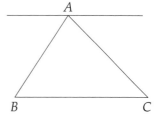

3. Use the angle sum of a triangle to prove that the sum of the angles in a polygon with n sides is $(n-2)180°$.

4. Show that the result about the angle sum of a polygon is true even if some of the internal angles are allowed to be greater than 180°.

5. If AB is parallel to CD, prove that

$$p + q + r = 180°.$$

With the same diagram, state the converse to this question. If the converse is true, prove it, and if not, say why it is false.

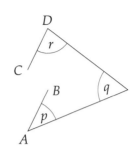

6. Prove that $b - a + x = 180°$.

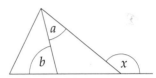

7. Prove that $x = a + b + c$.

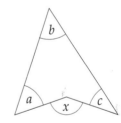

8. What is $a + b + c + d + e + f$?

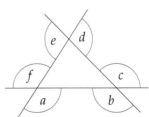

9. Find the sum of the internal angles at A, B, C, D and E.

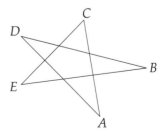

10. Find the sum of the internal angles at A, B, C, D, E, F, G and H.

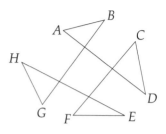

11. The lines AB and CD are parallel and a transversal meets them at P and Q. The angle bisectors of $\angle APQ$ and $\angle CQP$ meet at S, and those of $\angle BPQ$ and $\angle DQP$ meet at R.

    Prove that $PRQS$ is a rectangle.

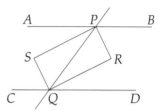

12. Each external angle of a regular polygon is one quarter of each internal angle. How many sides does the polygon have?

13. Each internal angle of a polygon is an obtuse angle which is a whole number of degrees. What is the greatest number of sides the polygon could have?

14. The sum of the internal angles of an n-gon is double the sum of the exterior angles. Find the value of n.

15. The diagram shows a regular pentagon and a regular hexagon which overlap.

    Find the value of x.

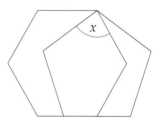

16. In $\triangle ABC$, the bisectors of the angles B and C meet at I. Prove that $2 \times \angle BIC - \angle A = 180°$.

17. If the side BC of $\triangle ABC$ is produced to D, the bisector of $\angle ACD$ is known as the *external bisector* of angle C. The internal bisector of $\angle B$ and the external bisector of $\angle C$ meet at P. Prove that $2 \times \angle BPC = \angle BAC$.

18. The bisector of $\angle A$ of $\triangle ABC$ meets BC at D. Let x be $\angle B$, y the external angle at C, and z be $\angle ADC$. Prove that $x + y = 2z$.

19. In a quadrilateral $ABCD$, let the bisectors of $\angle A$ and $\angle B$ meet at P and the bisectors at $\angle C$ and $\angle D$ meet at Q. Prove that $\angle APB + \angle CQD = 180°$.

20. The altitudes AD and BE of $\triangle ABC$ meet at H. Prove that $\angle AHB = \angle A + \angle B$.

21. For which pairs of values of m and n is it possible for the external angle of a regular m-gon to be equal to the internal angle of a regular n-gon?

You must prove that you have found *all* solutions.

Chapter 2

Congruent triangles

2.1 Congruence conditions

The four theorems which follow give conditions for the triangles $\triangle ABC$ and $\triangle PQR$ to be congruent. The symbol $\equiv$ is used for congruence, and the statement

$$\triangle ABC \equiv \triangle PQR$$

implies six equalities. Three of these concern the side lengths

$$AB = PQ \qquad BC = QR \qquad CA = RP$$

and three concern the angles

$$\angle ABC = \angle PQR \qquad \angle BCA = \angle QRP \qquad \angle CAB = \angle RPQ.$$

These facts can be read off without difficulty from the original statement, since the vertices of the two triangles are listed in corresponding order.

SSS

If $\qquad AB = PQ$
and $\qquad BC = QR$
and $\qquad CA = RP,$
then $\quad \triangle ABC \equiv \triangle PQR.$

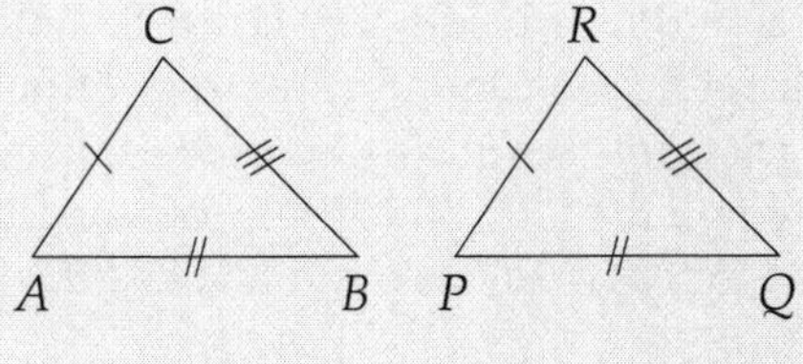

SAS

If $CA = RP$
and $\angle CAB = \angle RPQ$
and $AB = PQ,$
then $\triangle ABC \equiv \triangle PQR.$

ASA

If $\angle CAB = \angle RPQ$
and $AB = PQ$
and $\angle ABC = \angle PQR,$
then $\triangle ABC \equiv \triangle PQR.$

RHS

If $CA = RP$
and $AB = PQ$
and $\angle BCA = 90° = \angle QRP,$
then $\triangle ABC \equiv \triangle PQR.$

The angle in the SAS condition must be *between* the two sides; it is read as two sides and an *included* angle. We shall see later that this is important. Strictly speaking, the ASA condition requires that the two angles are at either end of the side. The fact that the angle sum of a triangle is constant means that we can interpret this condition in terms of *any* two angles of the triangle, "AAS", as long as the side is *corresponding* in the two diagrams. Although the RHS criterion is free-standing, it could have been introduced after Pythagoras' theorem is proved, when it becomes a special case of SSS.

2.2 Isosceles triangles

If a triangle is isosceles, the base angles are equal

If $AB = AC$, then $\angle ABC = \angle ACB$.

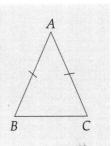

The four proofs which follow use the congruence criteria in different ways. Note particularly the fourth proof, which shows that the triangle is congruent to itself with the vertices listed in a different order.

PROOF ONE

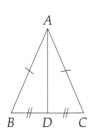

Let D be the *midpoint* of BC.

Then	$AB = AC$	(given)
and	$AD = AD$	(common side)
and	$BD = CD$	(by construction).
Therefore	$\triangle ABD \equiv \triangle ACD$	(SSS).
Therefore	$\angle ABD = \angle ACD$	
and so	$\angle ABC = \angle ACB.$	❏

PROOF TWO

Let AD be the *perpendicular* to BC.

Then	$AB = AC$	(given)
and	$AD = AD$	(common side)
and	$\angle ADB = \angle ADC$	(by construction).
Therefore	$\triangle ABD \equiv \triangle ACD$	(RHS).
Therefore	$\angle ABD = \angle ACD$	
and so	$\angle ABC = \angle ACB.$	❏

PROOF THREE

Let AD be the *bisector* of angle A.

Then	$AB = AC$	(given)
and	$AD = AD$	(common side)
and	$\angle BAD = \angle CAD$	(by construction).
Therefore	$\triangle ABD \equiv \triangle ACD$	(SAS).
Therefore	$\angle ABD = \angle ACD$	
and so	$\angle ABC = \angle ACB$.	

❑

PROOF FOUR

Consider $\triangle ABC$ and $\triangle ACB$.

Then	$AB = AC$	(given)
and	$AC = AB$	(given)
and	$BC = CB$	(same side).
Therefore	$\triangle ABC \equiv \triangle ACB$	(SSS).
Therefore	$\angle ABC = \angle ACB$.	

❑

We also have the converse result.

If the base angles are equal, a triangle is isosceles

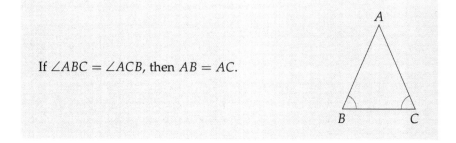

If $\angle ABC = \angle ACB$, then $AB = AC$.

This time we have three contrasting proofs.

PROOF ONE

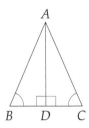

Let *AD* be *perpendicular* to *BC*.

Then $\angle ABD = \angle ACD$ (given)

and $AD = AD$ (common side)

and $\angle ADB = \angle ADC$ (by construction).

Therefore $\triangle ABD \equiv \triangle ACD$ (AAS).

Therefore $AB = AC$.   ❏

PROOF TWO

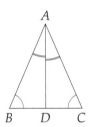

Let *AD* be the *bisector* of angle *A*.

Then $\angle ABD = \angle ACD$ (given)

and $AD = AD$ (common side)

and $\angle BAD = \angle CAD$ (by construction).

Therefore $\triangle ABD \equiv \triangle ACD$ (ASA).

Therefore $AB = AC$.   ❏

PROOF THREE

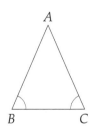

Consider $\triangle ABC$ and $\triangle ACB$.

Then $\angle ABC = \angle ACB$ (given)

and $\angle ACB = \angle ABC$ (given)

and $BC = CB$ (same side).

Therefore $\triangle ABC \equiv \triangle ACB$ (AAS).

Therefore $AB = AC$.   ❏

An obvious question is: what happened to the proof using the midpoint of the side *BC*. If you try to write down this argument, you will see that the information you have would require the use of ASS, where the angle is *not* included. The fact that the *result* is true does not allow the use of an invalid *proof*. The reason is that ASS can give rise to *results* which are false. Here is an example.

Consider an isosceles $\triangle ABC$. We shall assume the results above, so both $AB = AC$ and $\angle ABC = \angle ACB$.

Let D be *any* point on the base BC.

Then	$\angle ABD = \angle ACD$	(given)
and	$AB = AC$	(given)
and	$AD = AD$	(common side).
Therefore	$\triangle ABD \equiv \triangle ACD$	(ASS).
Therefore	$BD = DC$.	

This is clearly false. That is why one must be careful about using the congruence criteria rigorously.

It is worth making some points about the use of language.

- Strictly speaking, an *isosceles triangle* is one with two equal sides. Since this has been shown to be equivalent to having two equal angles, one tends to be rather lax and use the word to mean either alternative.
- Recall that a regular polygon is one with equal angles and equal sides. It is possible for a polygon to have equal sides without equal angles and for it to have equal angles without equal sides.
- This is not true for triangles. Again, being very precise, an *equilateral triangle* is one with three equal *sides*, and an *equiangular triangle* is one with three equal *angles*. As each of these properties implies the other, we tend to use the term 'equilateral' rather loosely to imply both of them at once.

A historical note   The result that the base angles of an isosceles triangle are equal, which was Euclid's fifth proposition, was known as the *pons asinorum* or the 'bridge of asses', since it functioned as a sort of barrier in the study of geometry which the unworthy would not be able to pass. Naturally users of this book will (as suggested by its title) have no problems in this respect!

Problems 2a

1. Give an example of a quadrilateral which has four equal angles, but which does not have four equal sides.

2. Give an example of a quadrilateral which has four equal sides, but which does not have four equal angles.

3. Prove that a triangle which has three equal sides has three equal angles.

4. Prove that a triangle which has three equal angles has three equal sides.

5. Prove that the triangle which is formed by joining the midpoints of the sides of an equilateral triangle is also equilateral.

6. The diagram shows two equal squares.

Prove that $x = 2y$.

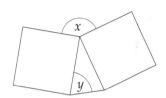

7. If $AB = AC$, prove that $y = x + z$.

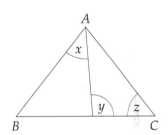

8. If $AB = AC$ and $DC = DA$, prove that $3x + y = 180°$.

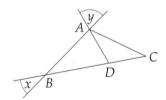

9. If $XY = XZ$, prove that $2y = x + z$.

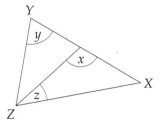

10. In the quadrilateral $ABCD$, angle ABC is $90°$ and $BA = BD = BC$.

Find the value of $a + b$.

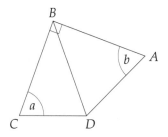

11. In the diagram, $PS = PR = QR$.

Prove that $4a + 3b = 540°$.

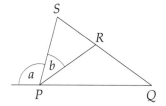

12. The parallelogram $KLMN$ is inscribed in $\triangle ABC$.

If $BK = KN$ and $ML = LC$, prove that BA is perpendicular to CA.

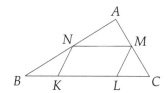

13. $ABCDE$ is a regular pentagon. The side BA is produced to F, so that $BA = AF$.

Find the ratio $x : y : z$.

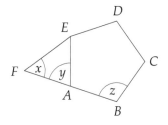

14. The diagram shows two equilateral triangles.

Find $a + b + c$.

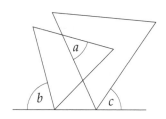

15. The diagram shows a regular
pentagon $ABCDE$ together with
three sides of a regular hexagon
$FDBGHJ$; points H and J are not
shown.

Find the value of $\angle ABG$.

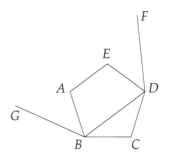

16. The diagram shows an irregular
hexagon with six equal angles.

Prove that $a + b = d + e$ and state
two similar equations.

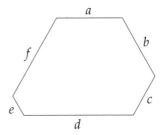

17. The lines AB and CD are parallel
and $BC = BD$. The acute angle x is
not equal to $60°$.

How many other angles in the figure
are equal to x?

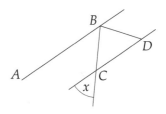

18. If $AD = DE = EC = CB$ and if
$AB = AC$, prove that

$$\angle BAC = \angle BCE.$$

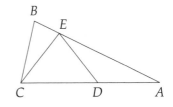

19. A regular hexagon has been divided
into four trapezia and one hexagon
as shown in the diagram.

If each of the five sections has the
same perimeter, find the ratio
$p : q : r$.

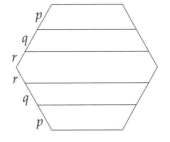

20. Ten stones, of identical shape and size, are used to make an arch. Each stone has a cross-section in the shape of an isosceles trapezium. Find the smallest angle of the trapezium.

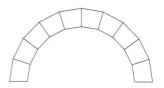

21. *ABCDEFGH* is a regular octagon. *P* is a point inside the octagon such that △*ABP* is equilateral. Find ∠*APC*.

22. *D* is the midpoint of the side *BC* of △*ABC*. If *AD* = *DB*, prove that ∠*A* = 90°.

23. In △*ABC*, *AB* = *AC* and *P* is any point on *BC* produced. *PX* and *PY* are the perpendiculars from *P* to *AB* and *AC* produced. Prove that ∠*XPB* = ∠*YPB*.

24. Points *X* and *Y* are taken in the base *BC* of △*ABC* so that ∠*BAX* is equal to ∠*CAY*. If *AX* = *AY*, prove that △*ABC* is isosceles.

25. In △*ABC*, ∠*B* = ∠*C* = 2 × ∠*A*, and the bisector of *B* meets *AC* at *X*. Prove that *AX* = *BX* = *BC*.

26. Both △*ABC* and △*APQ* are equilateral, and *P* is the midpoint of *BC*. Prove that *AC* and *PQ* are perpendicular.

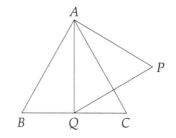

27. △*ABC* is right-angled at *B*, point *D* is the foot of the altitude from *B* to *AC*, and *AB* = *AE*.

Prove that *BE* is the bisector of ∠*DBC*.

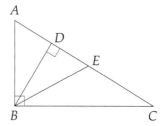

28. $\triangle ABC$ is equilateral. XY is parallel to AC, and Z is on AC produced so that $BY = CZ$.

Prove that XC is parallel to YZ.

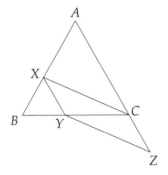

2.3 Properties of quadrilaterals

The congruence criteria are easily used to prove results about quadrilaterals. Most of these are 'obvious' and are sometimes assumed by 'appealing to symmetry'. However, they should be proved rigorously to ensure that the subject of geometry is based on firm foundations. Once they have been proved, they can then be assumed in subsequent work.

The importance of defining quadrilaterals carefully, in a minimal way, is discussed in the Preface. There are also some converse results, which enable us to identify particular types of quadrilateral from given information. For example, a quadrilateral with equal diagonals which bisect one another must be a rectangle, and must therefore share all the other properties of rectangles. The following exercise can be worked through quite quickly in order to establish these results. It is not necessary to use congruent triangles for every part. In addition, you may use the results of previous questions in those which follow.

Problems 2b

1. If $ABCD$ is a parallelogram, prove that
   (a) opposite sides are equal, that is, $AB = DC$ and $AD = BC$;
   (b) opposite angles are equal, in other words, $\angle BAD = \angle DCB$ and $\angle ABC = \angle CDA$.

2. If $ABCD$ is a quadrilateral, and AB is equal and parallel to DC, prove that it is a parallelogram.

3. If $ABCD$ is a quadrilateral, prove that

(a) if $AB = DC$ and $AD = BC$, it is a parallelogram;

(b) if $\angle BAD = \angle DCB$ and $\angle ABC = \angle CDA$, it is a parallelogram.

4. In $ABCD$, AB is equal to DC and AD is parallel to BC.

Comment on the following argument.

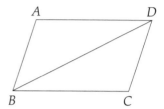

	$AB = CD$	(given)
and	$\angle ADB = \angle CBD$	(alternate)
and	$DB = BD$	(common).
Therefore	$\triangle ADB = \triangle CBD$	(SAS).
Therefore	$AD = CB$.	

Therefore ABCD is a parallelogram.

5. Prove that the diagonals of a parallelogram bisect one another.

6. Prove that, if the diagonals of a quadrilateral bisect one another, it is a parallelogram.

7. Prove that, in a kite

(a) one of the diagonals bisects the angles at the vertices,

(b) the diagonals are perpendicular,

(c) one of the diagonals bisects the other.

8. Prove that, in a rhombus

(a) all four sides are equal,

(b) the diagonals bisect the angles at the vertices,

(c) the diagonals bisect one another at right angles.

9. Prove that, in a rectangle

(a) all four angles are equal,

(b) the diagonals are equal and bisect one another.

10. Prove that, if a quadrilateral

   (a) has four equal sides, it is a rhombus;

   (b) has four equal angles, it is a rectangle;

   (c) is a rhombus with equal diagonals, it is a square;

   (d) is a rectangle with perpendicular diagonals, it is a square;

   (e) is a rectangle with a pair of equal adjacent sides, it is a square.

11. Prove that, if the diagonals of a quadrilateral

   (a) bisect the angles at the vertices, it is a rhombus;

   (b) bisect one another at right angles, it is a rhombus;

   (c) are equal and bisect one another, it is a rectangle.

12. Prove that a square has four equal sides and angles, and its diagonals are equal, bisect the angles at the vertices and bisect one another at right angles.

13. In quadrilateral $ABCD$, $AB = AD$ and $\angle ABC = \angle ADC$. Prove that $ABCD$ is a kite.

14. In quadrilateral $ABCD$, $AD = BC$ and $AC = BD$. Prove that $ABCD$ is a trapezium.

15. Prove that if a trapezium has the two non-parallel sides equal, then it has two pairs of equal adjacent angles.

Problems 2c

This exercise contains a variety of situations involving congruent triangles.

1. Let D be the midpoint of side BC of $\triangle ABC$, and let AD be produced to E so that $AD = DE$. Prove that $ACEB$ is a parallelogram.

2. Prove that, if two altitudes of a triangle are equal, it is isosceles.

3. (a) $\triangle ABC$ and $\triangle DBC$ are congruent triangles which are on opposite sides of the common side BC. Prove that BC bisects AD.

   (b) $\triangle ABC$ and $\triangle DCB$ are congruent triangles which are on opposite sides of the common side BC. Prove that BC bisects AD.

4. O is a point on the line AB. Equal lines OP and OQ are drawn so that $\angle POQ$ is $90°$. M and N are the feet of the perpendiculars from P and Q to AB. Prove that $PM = ON$.

5. $\triangle ABC$ is isosceles, with $AB = AC$, and D is a point, on the same side of BC as A, such that $DB = DC$. If $\angle BAC + \angle DBC = 90°$, prove that AD is equal to BC.

6. Draw equilateral triangles $\triangle ACP$ and $\triangle BAQ$ externally on the sides AC and BA of $\triangle ABC$. Prove that $BP = QC$.

7. In the diagram, $ABCD$ is a square and XY a straight line through A. DX and BY are perpendicular to XY.

   Prove that $DX + BY = XY$.

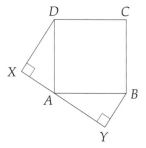

8. $\triangle ABC$ is right-angled at $\angle A$. Squares $BPQC$ and $CRSA$ are situated outside the triangle. Prove that AQ and BR are equal and perpendicular.

9. $\triangle ABC$ is equilateral. X, Y and Z are points on BC, CA and AB respectively so that $\triangle XYZ$ is also equilateral. Prove that $AY + AZ = BC$.

10. $ABCD$ is a parallelogram, and $\triangle CBX$ and $\triangle DCY$ are equilateral triangles situated outside the parallelogram. Prove that $\triangle AXY$ is also equilateral.

11. The point B_1 is the midpoint of side AC of $\triangle ABC$ and C_1 is the midpoint of AB. Prove that C_1B_1 is parallel to BC and half its length.

12. Let AA', BB' and CC' be three diameters of a circle. Prove that $\angle ABC$ is equal to $\angle A'B'C'$.

13. The diagram shows two isosceles triangles with $AB = AC$, $AB_1 = AC_1$ and $\angle BAC = \angle B_1AC_1$. Prove that $BB_1 = CC_1$.

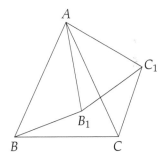

14. If D is the midpoint of BC, and BX and CY are both perpendicular to AY, prove that $BX = CY$.

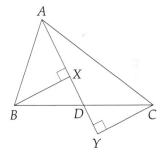

15. CX and CY are the internal and external bisectors of $\angle C$ of $\triangle ABC$, and XY is parallel to BC.

Prove that AC bisects XY.

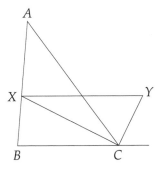

16. In the diagram, AD and CE are parallel, $AD = AB$ and $CB = CE$.

Prove that BD is perpendicular to BE.

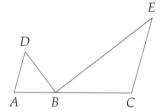

17. D is a point on the side BC of $\triangle ABC$, and both $\triangle ABD$ and $\triangle ACD$ are isosceles. Show that $\triangle ABC$ has at least one of the following three properties:

(a) It is right-angled.

(b) One of its angles is twice another angle.

(c) One of its angles is three times another angle.

18. Let P be any point on the base of $\triangle ABC$ with $AB = AC$, and let X and Y be the feet of the perpendiculars from P to AB and AC. Prove that $PX + PY$ is a constant.

19. In the diagram, P is the intersection of the perpendicular bisector of AB and the angle bisector of $\angle BCA$.

The points X and Y are the feet of the perpendiculars from P to BC and AC.

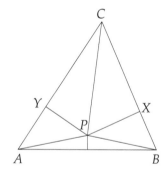

(a) Prove that $AP = PB$.

(b) Prove that $\triangle PYC \equiv \triangle PXC$ and hence that $CY = CX$.

(c) Prove that $\triangle PYA \equiv \triangle PXB$ and hence that $AY = BX$.

(d) Hence $AC = BC$.

Comment.

Chapter 3

Area

3.1 Polygons

The area of a rectangle is bh, where b is its base and h its height. Several other formulae follow from this.

Parallelogram

The area of a parallelogram is bh, where b is its base and h its vertical height.

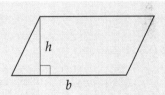

Triangle

The area of a triangle is $\frac{1}{2}bh$, where b is its base and h its vertical height.

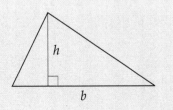

Trapezium

The area of a trapezium is $\frac{1}{2}(a+b)h$, where a and b are the lengths of the parallel sides and h is the vertical height.

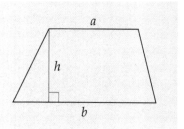

Kite

The area of a kite is $\frac{1}{2}pq$, where p and q are the lengths of the diagonals.

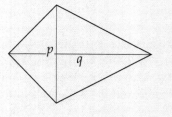

These results, along with many others concerning areas, are proved using dissection — dividing a large area up into smaller ones.

Problems 3a

1. Prove the formulae above. (You may, of course, assume the results from Chapter 2 about these quadrilaterals.)

2. Let $\triangle ABC$ be right-angled at A, and let the lengths AB, BC and CA be denoted by c, a and b. Let h denote the altitude from A to BC. Prove that $h = \frac{bc}{a}$.

3. In this regular octagon, of side 1, what is the difference between the area of the shaded region and the area of the unshaded region?

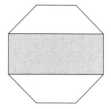

4. Three-quarters of the area of the rectangle has been shaded.

What is the value of x?

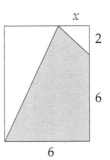

5. In the diagram, a corner of the shaded star is at the midpoint of each side of the large square.

What fraction of the large square is shaded?

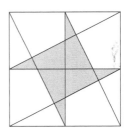

6. The diagram shows two squares, with sides of length 1 and 3, which have the same centre and corresponding sides parallel.

What fraction of the larger square is shaded?

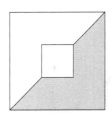

7. The diagram shows four overlapping squares which have sides 5, 7, 9 and 11.

What is the difference between the total area shaded grey and the total area shaded black?

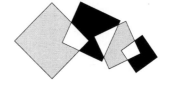

8. Five identical rectangles fit together as shown.

What is the total area?

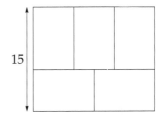

9. An equilateral triangle has its
vertices at the midpoints of alternate
sides of a regular hexagon.

What fraction of the area of the
hexagon is shaded?

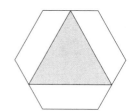

10. The diagram shows a right-angled
isosceles $\triangle ABC$ which
circumscribes a square $PQRS$.

What is the ratio $[PQRS] : [CAB]$?

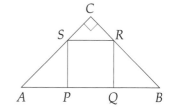

11. Prove that the area of the pentagon
shown is $\frac{1}{2}b(a+c)$.

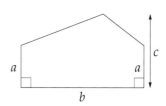

12. A square is divided up into four
congruent rectangles and a smaller
square, as shown. The area of the
small square is one quarter that of
the large square.

In what ratio are the sides of a
rectangle to one another?

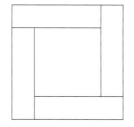

13. $ABCD$ is a rectangle. The length of
AP is one third of the length of AD
and BQ is one quarter of the length
of BC.

What is the ratio of the areas
$[ABQP] : [ABCD]$?

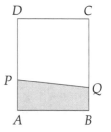

14. The diagram shows a regular
    hexagon of area 60.

    What is the area of the shaded kite?

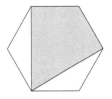

15. A square of side 2 is placed
    overlapping a 1 by 3 rectangle, so
    that one vertex of the square lies on
    a side of the rectangle, and the
    diagonals of the square are parallel
    to the sides of the rectangle.

    Find the area of the shaded triangle.

16. The outer equilateral triangle has
    area 1, and the points A, B and C
    are each one quarter of the way
    along the sides.

    What is the area of $\triangle ABC$?

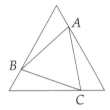

17. Two square pieces of card, each of side 3, are attached by a single pin
    to a board. The pin passes through a point $\frac{1}{3}$ of the way along the
    diagonal of each square and the squares overlap exactly. The bottom
    card now remains fixed, while the top card is rotated through 180°.
    What is the area of overlap of the cards in this new position?

18. A trapezium has parallel sides of lengths a and b and height h. The
    length of each parallel side is decreased by 10% and the height is
    increased by 10%. What is the resulting percentage change in the
    area?

3.2   Equal areas

Parallelograms

Parallelograms with the same base
and between the same parallels have
equal area.

$$[ABCD] = [EFCD]$$

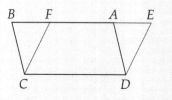

Triangles

(a) Triangles with the same base and
    between the same parallels have
    equal area.

$$[ABC] = [DBC]$$

(b) If two triangles on the same base
    have equal areas, then they lie
    between parallel lines.

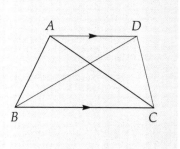

The last, converse, result can be particularly useful in certain proofs.

Problems 3b

1. The diagonals of a quadrilateral divide it into four triangles of equal
   area. What can be said about it?

2. The outer parallelogram is divided
   into four inner parallelograms which
   meet at a point on the diagonal.

   Prove that the grey and black
   parallelograms have equal areas.

3. In the same diagram as question 2, show that

   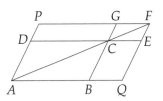

   (a) $[ABD] + [AEG] = [AQP]$,

   (b) $[ABCD] = [CEFG] + 2[PCQ]$.

4. In $\triangle ABC$, A_1 is the midpoint of side BC. Point X is any point on the median AA_1. Prove that

   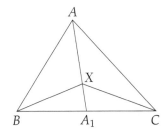

   (a) $[ABA_1] = [AA_1C]$,

   (b) $[XBA_1] = [XA_1C]$,

   (c) $[XAB] = [XCA]$.

5. Point P is a variable point within an equilateral $\triangle ABC$. Perpendiculars PX, PY and PZ are dropped onto sides AB, BC and CA respectively. Prove that $PX + PY + PZ$ is a constant.

   How can this result be modified if P lies outside the triangle?

6. $\triangle ABC$ is right-angled at A, the lengths of AC and AB are b and c, and a square of side length x is inscribed in the triangle with A at one corner. Prove that

   $$\frac{1}{b} + \frac{1}{c} = \frac{1}{x}.$$

7. In quadrilateral $ABCD$, points M, N lie on AB such that $AM = MN = NB$, and points P, Q lie on CD such that $CP = PQ = QD$. Prove that

   $$[AMCP] = [MNPQ] = \tfrac{1}{3}[ABCD].$$

8. The diagram shows a triangle divided into regions using lines from the vertices to points of trisection of the opposite sides.

   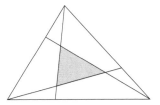

   Prove that the area of the shaded triangle is one seventh of the area of the whole triangle.

Chapter 4

Triangles: sides and angles

4.1 Right-angled triangles

Pythagoras' theorem

(a) If, in $\triangle ABC$, $\angle BAC = 90°$, then
$BA^2 + AC^2 = BC^2$.

(b) If, in $\triangle ABC$, $BA^2 + AC^2 = BC^2$, then
$\angle BAC = 90°$.

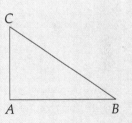

Problems 4a

There are many ways to prove Pythagoras' theorem and its converse, but the first in the exercise is the 'classic' diagram, and you are invited to complete the proof. This exercise provides an opportunity to prove the result in different ways. Further proofs of the theorem will be found in subsequent chapters.

1. Suppose that $\triangle ABC$ is right-angled at A. Construct squares on the sides as shown. Let AQP be perpendicular to BC and LK.

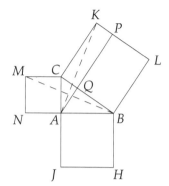

  (a) Prove that $\triangle ACK \equiv \triangle MCB$.

  (b) Prove that $[ACMN] = 2[MBC]$.

  (c) Prove that $[CQPK] = 2[CAK]$.

  (d) Prove that $[ACMN] = [PKCQ]$.

  (e) Prove that $[HBAJ] = [BLPQ]$.

  (f) Deduce Pythagoras' theorem.

2. Now we prove the converse. Suppose that, in $\triangle ABC$, we have $BA^2 + AC^2 = BC^2$. Let $\triangle XYZ$ be a triangle with $YX = BA$, $XZ = AC$ and $\angle ZXY = 90°$.

  (a) Prove that $YZ = BC$.

  (b) Hence show that $\triangle ABC$ is congruent to $\triangle XYZ$.

  (c) Hence prove that $\angle BAC = 90°$.

3. The top diagram shows a square, in which is inscribed four copies of a right-angled triangle with sides a, b and c.

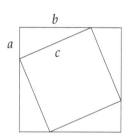

  (a) Prove that the quadrilateral formed inside the four triangles is a square.

In the bottom diagram, the four triangles have been moved together to create two rectangles.

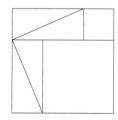

  (b) Prove that the other two quadrilaterals formed in this figure are squares.

  (c) Prove Pythagoras' theorem.

4. Inscribe four copies of a right-angled triangle into a square.

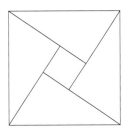

(a) Check that the triangles fit as shown, and that the central quadrilateral is a square.

(b) Use an algebraic method based on areas to deduce Pythagoras' theorem.

5. The diagram shows two copies of a right angled triangle arranged inside a quadrilateral.

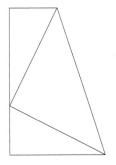

(a) Show that the quadrilateral is a trapezium and the other triangle is isosceles and right-angled.

(b) Use an algebraic method based on areas to deduce Pythagoras' theorem.

Problems 4b

1. In the right-angled $\triangle ABC$, $BD = 8$, $AD = 10$ and $AD = DC$.

Find the area of $\triangle ADC$.

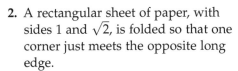

2. A rectangular sheet of paper, with sides 1 and $\sqrt{2}$, is folded so that one corner just meets the opposite long edge.

What is the value of d?

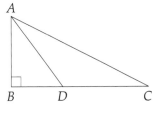
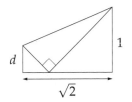

3. The diagram shows three right-angled triangles.

What is the value of x?

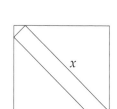

4. The diagram shows a $1 \times x$ rectangular plank which fits neatly inside a 10×10 square frame.

What is the value of x?

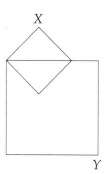

5. The diagram shows two superimposed squares. The one with vertex X has side 2 and that with vertex Y has side 4.

Calculate the length XY.

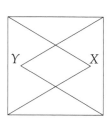

6. The diagram shows a square of side 1 and two equilateral triangles.

What is the distance XY?

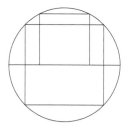

7. The diagram shows a square of area x inscribed inside a semicircle and a larger square of area y inscribed inside a circle.

What is the value of $\dfrac{x}{y}$?

8. Eight identical regular octagons are placed edge to edge in a ring in such a way that a symmetrical star shape is formed by the interior edges.

   If each octagon has sides of length 1, what is the area of the star?

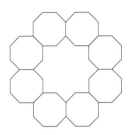

9. In $\triangle ABC$, AD is the altitude from A to BC. Show that $CD^2 + AB^2 = BD^2 + AC^2$.

10. In $\triangle ABC$, AD is the altitude from A to BC. If $AD^2 = CD \times DB$, show that $\triangle ABC$ is right-angled.

11. The diagonals of the quadrilateral $ABCD$ are at right angles. Show that $AB^2 + CD^2 = AD^2 + BC^2$.

12. $ABCD$ is a rhombus. Show that $AC^2 + BD^2 = 4AB^2$.

13. O is a point inside a rectangle $ABCD$. Show that $AO^2 + CO^2 = BO^2 + DO^2$.

14. $\triangle ABC$ is right-angled at C, and the altitude from C to AB has length h. Show that, in the usual notation,

$$\frac{1}{h^2} = \frac{1}{a^2} + \frac{1}{b^2}.$$

4.2 Triangles without right angles

This section assumes familiarity with some ideas from school trigonometry, including the extension of sine and cosine to angles greater than 90°. Both rules are easily proved by dropping a perpendicular from A to BC, though the cosine rule really requires two diagrams, depending on whether the foot of the perpendicular is between B and C or not.

Sine and cosine rules

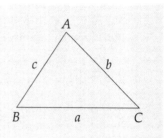

$$\frac{a}{\sin A} = \frac{b}{\sin B} = \frac{c}{\sin C}$$

$$a^2 = b^2 + c^2 - 2bc \cos A$$

Apollonius' median theorem

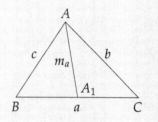

If m_a is the length of the median AA_1
from A to BC, then

$$2(b^2 + c^2) = a^2 + 4m_a^2.$$

Problems 4c

1. How does the cosine rule $a^2 = b^2 + c^2 - 2bc \cos A$ relate to Pythagoras' theorem (and its converse) if the angle A is

   (a) acute,

   (b) a right angle,

   (c) obtuse?

2. $ABCD$ is a trapezium, with AB parallel to DC. Show that
$$AC^2 + BD^2 = AD^2 + 2AB \times CD + BC^2.$$

3. D is a point on the base BC of an isosceles $\triangle ABC$. Show that
$$AB^2 = AD^2 + BD \times CD.$$

4. Prove Apollonius' median theorem.

5. Show that, for any triangle, the ratio

$$m_a^2 + m_b^2 + m_c^2 : a^2 + b^2 + c^2$$

is a constant, which should be stated.

6. Suppose that M divides the side BC of $\triangle ABC$ in the ratio $\lambda : \mu$. Show that

$$\mu AB^2 + \lambda AC^2 = (\lambda + \mu) AM^2 + \mu BM^2 + \lambda CM^2.$$

7. $\triangle PQR$ is right-angled at Q and $PQ = QR$. The line through Q which divides the angle PQR in the ratio $1 : 2$ meets PR at S. What is the ratio $RS : SP$?

8. The black triangle is drawn and squares are drawn externally on each of its sides. The three grey triangles are then formed as shown, and squares added externally on their 'new' sides. If the total area of the inner three squares is A and the total area of the outer three squares is B, what is the ratio $B : A$?

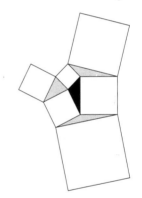

4.3 Solving triangles

The sine and cosine rules are normally used for finding missing angles and lengths in triangles. This is not the place to review what should be familiar work from the school curriculum, but it is worth making connections between this process of 'solving' triangles and the theorems about congruent triangles. The standard abbreviations are used to show what information is given about a triangle.

SSS   The triangle is uniquely determined, and the angles can be found using the cosine rule. There is no ambiguity about whether a particular angle is acute or obtuse, since this is shown by the sign of the cosine.

SAS   The triangle is uniquely determined. The third side can be found using the cosine rule; now the situation reverts to SSS. Alternatively, the sine rule can be used, but it is best to find the smaller of the two missing angles first (opposite the shorter side), since this must be acute, so there is no ambiguity.

RHS   There is no point in using either rule. Note that both remaining angles must be acute.

ASA   The third angle can be found from the angle sum, and now the sine rule determines the two missing sides.

ASS   This is not a congruence condition, since it does not necessarily determine the triangle uniquely. However, it is worth considering this in a little more detail.

The ambiguous case

If we are given the side lengths a and c and the angle $\angle A$, then it is (sometimes) the case that there are two positions for C, since the circle with centre B and radius a cuts AD twice.

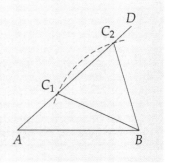

This result is reflected in the sine rule by the fact that we can determine $\sin C$ from the information given, but this gives both an acute and an obtuse value for the angle. However, it is worth noting that this situation does not *always* occur. The next set of problems examines it more closely, and refers to the diagram shown above.

Problems 4d

1. Prove geometrically that, if there are two intersections, $\angle BC_1A + \angle BC_2A = 180°$.

2. What is the *smallest* value of a which produces a triangle? What happens to the sine rule calculation if a takes this value? What happens if the value of a is smaller?

3. What is the *largest* value of a which produces a triangle? What happens to the sine rule calculation if a takes this value? What happens if the value of a is greater?

4. Under what restrictions on the sides and angles of the triangles involved does ASS lead to a valid congruence condition?

Chapter 5

Similarity

5.1 Similar triangles

Two triangles $\triangle ABC$ and $\triangle A'B'C'$ are similar if their angles are equal in pairs. In other words

$$\angle ABC = \angle A'B'C' \qquad \angle BCA = \angle B'C'A' \qquad \angle CAB = \angle C'A'B'.$$

We write $\triangle ABC \sim \triangle A'B'C'$, and note that the order of the vertices is important.

Similar triangles and ratios of sides

If $\triangle ABC$ and $\triangle A'B'C'$ are such that

$$\triangle ABC \sim \triangle A'B'C,$$

then

$$\frac{AB}{A'B'} = \frac{BC}{B'C'} = \frac{CA}{C'A'}.$$

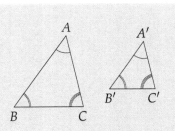

If $\triangle ABC$ and $\triangle A'B'C'$ are such that

$$\frac{AB}{A'B'} = \frac{BC}{B'C'} = \frac{CA}{C'A'},$$

then $\triangle ABC \sim \triangle A'B'C.$

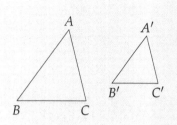

If $\triangle ABC$ and $\triangle A'B'C'$ are such that

$$\angle BAC = \angle B'A'C'$$

and $$\frac{AB}{A'B'} = \frac{CA}{C'A'},$$

then $\triangle ABC \sim \triangle A'B'C.$

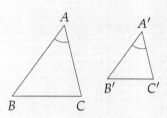

We will always respect the order convention here, since it gives the quickest way of setting up the ratio equations. For example, if we write $\triangle ABC \sim \triangle PQR$ with the angles lined up in order, then $\frac{AB}{PQ} = \frac{AC}{PR}$ since the letters all correspond. The proofs of these results are straightforward, but slightly fiddly, and they are omitted in this book.

It is also possible to talk about similar polygons (or, indeed, other shapes). However, it is not true that two polygons with equal angles must have corresponding sides in proportion — one need only think of two rectangles. The *definition* of similarity now requires both that angles are equal and that sides are in proportion. Hence the focus here is on similar *triangles*.

Problems 5a

1. A square is inscribed in a 3-4-5 right-angled triangle.

   What fraction of the area of the triangle does it occupy?

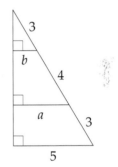

2. In this diagram, what is the value of $a + b$?

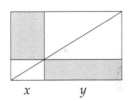

3. In terms of x and y, what proportion of this rectangle is shaded?

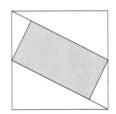

4. The diagram shows a square with two lines from a corner to the midpoint of the opposite side.

   What fraction of the area of square is occupied by the shaded rectangle?

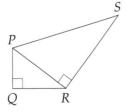

5. In the figure shown, $PQ = 2\frac{1}{3}$, $PS = 6\frac{6}{7}$ and $\angle QPR = \angle RPS$.

   Find the length of PR.

6. In the trapezium shown, XY is parallel to two sides and passes through the point of intersection of the diagonals.

What is the length of XY?

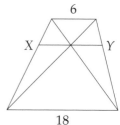

7. Let $\triangle ABC$ be right-angled at C, and CD be the perpendicular from C to AB.

  (a) Show that $\triangle ABC \sim \triangle CBD \sim \triangle ACD$.

  (b) Hence express x and y in terms of a, b and c.

  (c) Hence prove Pythagoras' theorem.

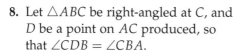

8. Let $\triangle ABC$ be right-angled at C, and D be a point on AC produced, so that $\angle CDB = \angle CBA$.

  (a) Express x and y in terms of a, b and c.

  (b) Hence, using the areas of $\triangle ABC$, $\triangle BCD$ and $\triangle ABD$, prove Pythagoras' theorem.

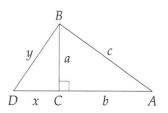

9. Let $\triangle ABC$ be right-angled at C, and $BD = BC = BE$.

Prove that $\angle DCE = 90°$ and hence that $\triangle ADC$ and $\triangle ACE$ are similar.

Use this to prove Pythagoras' theorem.

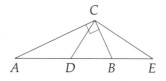

10. Let $\triangle ABC$ and $\triangle A'B'C'$ be similar (in the order given). Show that

$$\frac{[ABC]}{[A'B'C']} = \left(\frac{AB}{A'B'}\right)^2.$$

11. $\triangle ABC$ is isosceles with $AB = AC$, and D is the midpoint of AB. If $\angle BCD = \angle BAC = \theta$, what is the value of $\cos\theta$?

5.2 Intercept theorems

Midpoint theorem

Let B_1 and C_1 be the midpoints of the sides AC and AB of $\triangle ABC$. Then C_1B_1 is parallel to BC and half its length.

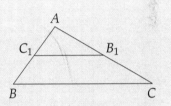

Intercept theorem

(a) If XY is parallel to BC, then
$$\frac{AX}{XB} = \frac{AY}{YC}.$$

(b) If
$$\frac{AX}{XB} = \frac{AY}{YC},$$
then XY is parallel to BC.

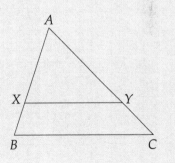

Problems 5b

1. Prove the midpoint theorem and the intercept theorem and its converse.

2. The midpoints of the sides of a quadrilateral are joined. Show that this produces a parallelogram whose area is half that of the quadrilateral.

3. Let $ABCD$ be a quadrilateral with equal and perpendicular diagonals (sometimes called a *pseudo-square*). Let P, Q, R and S be the midpoints of AB, BC, CD and DA. Prove that $PQRS$ is a square.

4. Let $ABCD$ be a quadrilateral with AD equal and perpendicular to CB, and let P, Q, R and S be the midpoints of AB, AC, CD and BD. Prove that $PQRS$ is a square.

5. Let $ABCD$ be a trapezium, with AB parallel to CD, and let P, Q, R and S be the midpoints of AC, BC, AD and BD. Prove that P, Q, R and S are collinear.

6. Let X be any point on the altitude AD of $\triangle ABC$. Let P, Q and R be the midpoints of BX, BA and AC. Show that $\angle PQR$ is a right angle.

7. Let P and Q be the midpoints of the medians BB_1 and CC_1 of $\triangle ABC$. Prove that PQ is parallel to BC and find $PQ : BC$.

8. Let P and Q be the feet of the perpendiculars from A to the angle bisectors of B and C of $\triangle ABC$. Prove that PQ is parallel to BC.

5.3 Angle bisectors

Angle bisector theorem

(a) Let AD and AE be the internal and external bisectors of $\angle A$ in $\triangle ABC$. Then

$$\frac{BD}{DC} = \frac{BA}{AC} = \frac{BE}{EC}.$$

(b) If D is a point on the base BC (or BC produced) of $\triangle ABC$ such that

$$\frac{BD}{DC} = \frac{BA}{AC},$$

then AD bisects $\angle A$ internally or externally.

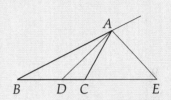

Problems 5c

1. Let AD be the internal bisector of angle A in $\triangle ABC$. Construct a line through C parallel to DA meeting BA at X.

  (a) Use parallel properties of angles to show that $\triangle XAC$ is isosceles.

  (b) Use the intercept theorem to prove the angle bisector theorem in the internal case.

  (c) Modify this argument to prove the external case.

  (d) Prove the converse.

2. Alternatively, show that

$$\frac{BD}{DC} = \frac{[ABD]}{[ACD]} = \frac{DP \times AB}{DQ \times AC},$$

where P and Q are the feet of the perpendiculars from D to AB and AC respectively. Use this to prove the theorem and its converse.

3. $\triangle PQR$ is right-angled at Q and $\angle QPR = 60°$. The bisector of $\angle QPR$ meets QR at S.

   What is the ratio $QS : SR$?

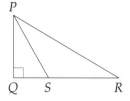

4. In the parallelogram $ABCD$, the bisector of $\angle BAD$ meets BD at P and CD at Q. Prove that $AP : PQ = BA : AD$.

5. In the quadrilateral $ABCD$, $AB = AD$. The bisectors of $\angle CAB$ and $\angle CAD$ meet CB and CD respectively at P and Q. Prove that PQ is parallel to BD.

6. In quadrilateral $ABCD$, show that the bisectors of $\angle B$ and $\angle D$ meet on AC if, and only if, the bisectors of A and C meet on BD.

7. In parallelogram $ABCD$, the bisector of $\angle A$ meets BD at P and the bisector of $\angle B$ meets AC at Q. Prove that PQ is parallel to AB.

Chapter 6

Triangles and inequalities

6.1 Angles and sides

In $\triangle ABC$,

(a) if $AC > AB$, then
$\angle ABC > \angle ACB$;

(b) if $\angle ABC > \angle ACB$, then
$AC > AB$.

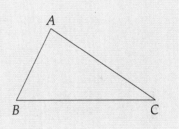

This says that the largest angle of a triangle is opposite the largest side, and *vice versa*.

Problems 6a

1. Suppose that $AB < AC$. Let D be a point on AC with $AD = AB$. Note that D must lie between A and C.

Prove that $\angle ABC > \angle ACB$.

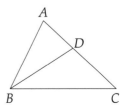

2. Prove the converse of this result by assuming that $AB \geq AC$ and deriving a contradiction.

3. Without assuming Pythagoras' theorem, prove that the shortest distance from a point A to a line ℓ is the perpendicular distance.

4. In $\triangle ABC$, $AB = AC$. Produce BA to a point X. Prove that $XB > XC$.

5. In $\triangle ABC$, $AB = AC$. Let X be an internal point of BC and produce BC to a point Y. Prove that $AX < AC < AY$.

6. In $\triangle ABC$, the bisector of $\angle BAC$ meets BC at X. Prove that BA is greater than BX.

7. In $\triangle ABC$, $AB > AC$. Let the bisectors of the angles at B and C meet at I. Prove that $IB > IC$.

8. In the convex quadrilateral $ABCD$, the angles at B and D are equal and $AB > AD$. Prove that $CB < CD$.

6.2 The triangle inequality

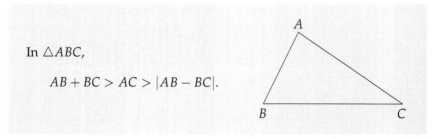

In $\triangle ABC$,

$$AB + BC > AC > |AB - BC|.$$

This states the intuitively obvious fact that a straight line is the shortest distance between two points. It has many more significant consequences than you might think. Sometimes it is stated using $\geq$ rather than strict inequalities. This allows for 'degenerate' triangles in which A, B and C are collinear.

Problems 6b

1. In $\triangle ABC$, produce CB to D, where $BD = BA$.

   Show that $\angle CAD > \angle CDA$ and hence prove the left-hand part of the triangle inequality.

   Use this to obtain the right-hand part.

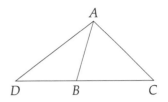

2. In a quadrilateral, prove that the sum of any three sides is greater than the fourth.

3. $\triangle ABC$ has perimeter p; let $s = \frac{1}{2}p$ be the *semi-perimeter*. Let D be any point on the side BC; prove that $AD < s$.

4. If, in quadrilateral $ABCD$, AB is the shortest side and CD the greatest, prove that $\angle A > \angle C$ and $\angle B > \angle D$.

5. Show that, if P is a point external to a circle, then the shortest and longest distances from P to the circle lie along the diameter through P.

6. Let P be an interior point of a convex quadrilateral $ABCD$. Prove that $PA + PB + PC + PD \geq AC + BD$, and give a condition for equality.

7. Let m_a be the length of the median of $\triangle ABC$ from A to BC. Prove that $2m_a < b + c$ and that $m_a + m_b + m_c < p$, the perimeter of $\triangle ABC$.

8. Let a quadrilateral $ABCD$ have perimeter p. Prove that $s < AC + BD < p$.

9. Let O be any point in the plane of the square $ABCD$. Prove that $OA < OB + OC + OD$.

10. Let P be an interior point of $\triangle ABC$ with perimeter p. Prove that $s < PA + PB + PC < p$.

Chapter 7

Circles and angles

7.1 Symmetry properties

In the following, O always denotes the centre of a circle.

Chords and radii

(a) If X is the midpoint of AB, then OX is perpendicular to AB.

(b) If OX is perpendicular to AB, then X is the midpoint of AB.

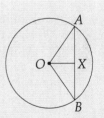

Distances from centre

(a) If $AB = CD$, then AB and CD are equidistant from O.

(b) If AB and CD are equidistant from O, then $AB = CD$.

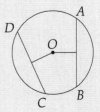

Problems 7a

   1. Prove the results above.

   2. A line bisects the chord of a circle at right angles. Prove that it passes through the centre of the circle.

   3. Prove that equal chords of a circle subtend the same angle at O.

   4. State and prove the converse of the result in question 3.

   5. A line cuts two concentric circles at P, Q, R and S (in that order). Prove that $PQ = RS$.

   6. Two circles, with centres O_1 and O_2 meet at A and B. Show that O_1O_2 bisects AB at right angles.

   7. AB and AC are equal chords of a circle. Prove that O lies on the bisector of $\angle BAC$.

   8. AB and CD are parallel chords of a circle. Prove that the line joining their midpoints passes through O.

   9. A parallelogram is inscribed in a circle. Prove that it is a rectangle.

   10. A is a fixed point and m is a fixed line, which does not pass through A. Prove that all circles which pass through A and have their centre on m pass through another fixed point.

   11. Two circles, centres O_1 and O_2 intersect at P. The radii O_1Q and O_1P are parallel to radii O_2P and O_2R.

   Show that Q, P and R are collinear.

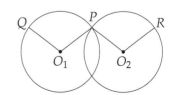

   12. PQ and RS are parallel lines which pass through the points of intersection of two circles.

   Prove that $PQ = RS$.

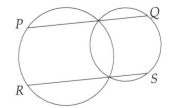

13. AB and CD are two equal chords of a circle, which intersect at X.

Prove that AX is equal to either CX or DX.

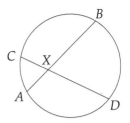

14. X is one of the intersections of two circles with centres A and B, and C is the midpoint of AB. A line through X, perpendicular to XC, meets the circles at P and Q. Prove that X is the midpoint of PQ.

7.2 Angle properties

Angle at the centre

The angle subtended at the centre by a chord is twice the angle subtended at the circumference.

$$\angle AOB = 2 \times \angle ACB$$

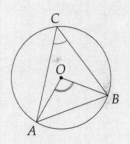

Angles in the same segment

Angles in the same segment are equal.

$$\angle AC_1B = \angle AC_2B$$

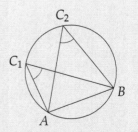

Angle in a semicircle

The angle in a semicircle is a right angle.

$$\angle ACB = 90°$$

(This is sometimes called *Thales' theorem*.)

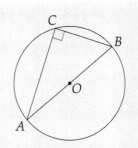

Opposite angles

The opposite angles of a cyclic quadrilateral add to 180°.

$$\angle ABC + \angle ADC = 180°$$

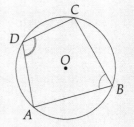

The following corollary is often useful.

External angle of a cyclic quadrilateral

The external angle of a cyclic quadrilateral is equal to the opposite internal angle.

$$\angle CBE = \angle CDA$$

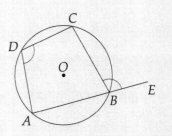

Problems 7b

1. Extend the line CO to P.

   (a) Prove that
       $$\angle AOP = \angle ACO + \angle OAC.$$

   (b) Hence prove the theorem about the angle at the centre.

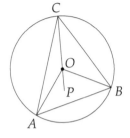

2. Modify the proof in question 1 to deal with the case when the triangles $\triangle AOB$ and $\triangle ACB$ overlap, as shown in the diagram.

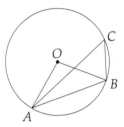

3. Use the 'angle at the centre' result to prove the theorem about angles in the same segment.

4. Prove the theorem about the angle in a semicircle.

5. Prove the theorems about cyclic quadrilaterals.

6. Find the size of the marked angle in the regular dodecagon.

7. O is the centre of a circle and the chords AB and DC meet at an external point X. Prove that

$$2 \times \angle AXD = \angle AOD - \angle BOC.$$

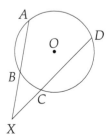

8. In the triangle shown,
$AC = BC = DC$.

What is the size of $\angle BAD$?

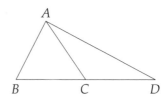

9. The smaller circle has radius 10 and
AB is a diameter. The larger circle
has centre A and radius 12, and the
two circles cut at C.

Find the length of BC.

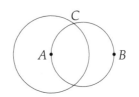

10. All six vertices of hexagon $UVWXYZ$ lie on the circumference of a
circle. Prove that $\angle XYZ + \angle ZUV + \angle VWX = 360°$.

11. A square $XABD$ of side length 1 is drawn inside a circle of diameter
XY of length 2. The point A lies on the circumference of the circle.
Another square $YCBE$ is drawn. What is the ratio of the areas of the
two squares?

12. $ABCD$ is cyclic and AB is parallel to DC. If $\angle ABC = 2 \times \angle BAC$,
prove that $\triangle ADC$ is isosceles.

13. $ABCD$ is a cyclic quadrilateral. AC and BD meet at Q, and DA and
CB, both produced, meet at P. Given that $CD = CP = DQ$, prove
that $\angle CAD = 60°$.

14. A and B are fixed points on a circle, and X is a variable point on
the arc AB. Prove that the angle bisector of $\angle AXB$ always passes
through a fixed point.

7.3   Converse results

Angles in the same segment

If C_1 and C_2 are points on the same side of
AB, and $\angle AC_1B = \angle AC_2B$, then the four
points A, B, C_1 and C_2 are concyclic.

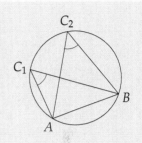

Angle in a semicircle

The circumcircle of a $\triangle ABC$ with
$\angle ACB = 90°$ has diameter AB.

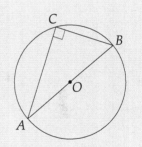

Opposite angles

If $\angle ABC + \angle ADC = 180°$, then the
quadrilateral $ABCD$ is cyclic.

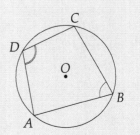

These results are important, since they allow us to deduce, from known angles in a figure, that four points lie on a circle, and we can then use the angle properties of that circle to show that other unknown angles are equal.

Problems 7c

1. Suppose that A, B, C_1 and C_2 are points such that $\angle AC_1B = \angle AC_2B$.

   Construct the circle through A, B and C_2, which intersects AC_1 at a point C_3.

   What can be said about $\angle AC_3B$?

   What follows?

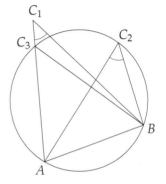

2. Prove the other converse theorems.

3. Explain why the 'angle at the centre' theorem does not have a converse.

4. $ABCD$ is a square and P any point on the diagonal AC. The lines XY and UV are parallel to AB and AD respectively.

   Prove that $XUYV$ is cyclic.

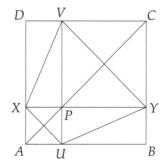

5. AOB is the diameter of a circle, and PQ is a perpendicular chord. Point X is any point on AB, and PX meets the circle again at Y.

   Prove that $YXOQ$ is cyclic.

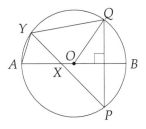

6. The altitudes AD and BE of $\triangle ABC$ meet at H.
   (a) Prove that $\angle DCH = \angle DEH$.
   (b) Prove that $\angle DEB = \angle DAB$.
   (c) Hence prove that CH is perpendicular to AB.

   This shows that the altitudes AD, BE and CF of a triangle are concurrent in a point H, which is called the *orthocentre* of $\triangle ABC$.

7. The altitudes AD and BE of $\triangle ABC$ meet at H, and C_1 is the mid-point of AB. Prove that $C_1E = C_1D$.

8. Two circles C_1 and C_2 intersect at X and Y. Points A and P are on C_1 and B and Q are points on C_2 such that A, Y and B are collinear. If AP and BQ meet at R, prove that P, X, Q and R are concyclic.

9. AOB is a diameter of a circle and X is any point on the circle. The line BX, produced if necessary, cuts the line through O perpendicular to AB at Y. Prove that $AOXY$ is cyclic.

10. $ABCE$ is a quadrilateral.

    If $CA = CB$, $EA = ED$ and $\angle EAC = \angle DAB$, prove that EC is parallel to AB.

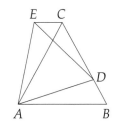

11. In the diagram, APC and BPD are straight lines, and BP and CP are diameters of their respective circles.

    Prove that the circle on diameter BC passes through A and D.

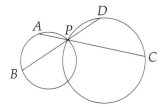

12. *ABCD* is a rectangle, *P* is the midpoint of *AB*, and *Q* is the point on *PD* such that *CQ* is perpendicular to *PD*. Prove that $\triangle BQC$ is isosceles.

13. Let *AB* be a diameter of a circle and *C, D* any points on the circumference on opposite sides of *AB*. The chord *CD* meets *AB* at *P*, and *E* and *F* are points on *AC* and *BD* such that *EPF* is perpendicular to *AB*.

Prove that $EP = PF$.

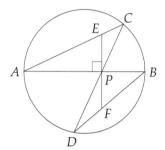

This is known as the *butterfly theorem*.

7.4   Congruence properties

It is an obvious fact that **circles of equal radius are congruent**. This means that the symmetry and angle properties can (with care) be transferred *between* circles of equal radius. For instance

Equal circles

(a) In two equal circles, equal chords are at equal distances from the centres.

(b) In two equal circles, chords at equal distances from the centres are equal.

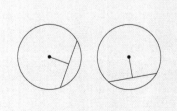

Since a circle is congruent to itself, this approach yields a group of important (but often overlooked) results.

Note that, since arc length is proportional to angle subtended at the centre, we can interpret angle results in terms of arcs, and also that these results can be taken to refer either to the angles at the centre or the circumference.

Equal arcs

Equal arcs subtend equal angles.

If arc $AB = $ arc CD, then $\angle AXB = \angle CYD$.

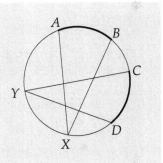

Equal chords

Equal chords subtend equal angles.

If $AB = CD$, then $\angle AXB = \angle CYD$.

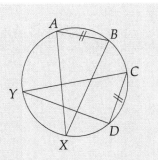

Equal angles

(a) Equal angles are subtended by equal chords.

(b) Equal angles are subtended by equal arcs.

If $\angle AXB = \angle CYD$, then
arc AB = arc CD and $AB = CD$.

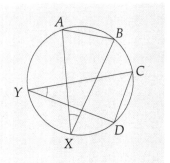

Problems 7d

1. Prove that a quadrilateral, with a pair of opposite sides equal, inscribed in a circle, must have equal diagonals.

2. Two equal circles meet at A and B. The line CAD has point C on one circle and D on the other. Prove that $BC = BD$.

3. Two equal circles meet at A. The lines CAD and EAF have C and E on one circle and D and F on the other. Prove that $CE = DF$.

4. $\triangle ABC$ is inscribed in a circle. Point E is the midpoint of the arc subtended by BC, on the opposite side from A, and ED is a diameter. Prove that $2 \times DEA = |\angle B - \angle C|$.

5. $ABCDEF$ is a hexagon inscribed in a circle.

   If AB is parallel to DE, and BC is parallel to EF, prove that CD is parallel to FA.

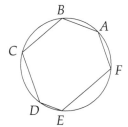

6. AB and AC are equal chords of a circle and BC is produced to D so that $CD = CA$. If DA cuts the circle at E, prove that $AE = CE$.

7. Two circles intersect at P and Q. Point X is a point on one circle, and Y, Z are points on the other circle such that XPY and XQZ are straight lines. Prove that the length of YZ is constant as X varies.

8. In the cyclic quadrilateral $ABCD$, the diagonal AC bisects $\angle DAB$. The side AD is extended beyond D to a point E. Prove that $CE = CA$ if, and only if, $DE = AB$.

9. In the cyclic quadrilateral $ABCD$, $\angle BAC = \angle CAD$.

   (a) Show that $\triangle BAC$ is congruent to $\triangle DAC$ if, and only if, AC is a diameter of the circle.

   (b) If AC is not a diameter, what is the relationship between $\triangle BAC$ and $\triangle DAC$?

Chapter 8

Loci and constructions

8.1 Loci

The locus of a point is the path (or region) traced out when it moves in accordance with some given law. In this book, we restrict ourselves to plane geometry, in two dimensions, but the concept of locus is easily extended to three. This important geometrical concept is best illustrated by means of examples.

Circle

A point P moves so that its distance from a fixed point O is a constant a.

The locus of P is the circumference of a circle with centre O and radius a.

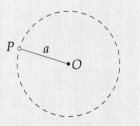

Parallel lines

A point P moves so that its distance from a fixed line AB is a constant a. (Here we are talking about *perpendicular* distance.)

The locus of P is two straight lines parallel to AB, at a distance of a either side of it. (We are thinking of AB as if it were an infinite line, so we are not worried about what happens 'at the ends'.)

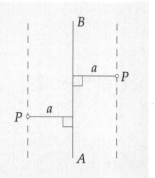

Perpendicular bisector

A point P moves so that it is an equal distance from two fixed points A and B.

The locus of P is the perpendicular bisector of AB, passing through M, the midpoint of AB.

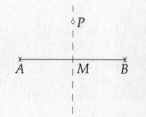

Angle bisectors

A point P moves so that it is an equal distance from two fixed lines AOB and COD.

The locus of P is the pair of lines which bisect the angles between AOB and COD.

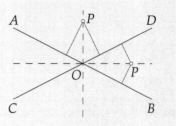

Problems 8a

In this exercise, you must not only describe the desired locus, but also prove that it *is* the locus.

1. Prove the result about the perpendicular bisector.

2. Prove the result about the angle bisectors.

3. A and B are two fixed points. A point P moves so that the area of $\triangle ABP$ is constant. Find the locus of P.

4. A is a fixed point, and the point P moves along a fixed straight line m. Find the locus of the midpoint of AP.

5. A is a fixed point, and the point P moves around the circumference of a fixed circle C. Find the locus of the midpoint of AP.

6. C is a fixed circle; find the locus of the midpoint of a variable chord of constant length.

7. Points A and B are fixed, and P is the centre of a variable circle which passes through A and B. Find the locus of P.

8. Find the locus of the centre of a variable circle which cuts off chords of equal lengths on two intersecting lines.

9. A and B are fixed points on a fixed line m. The line n passes through B, and is allowed to rotate. Point Q is the foot of the perpendicular from A to n. Find the locus of the midpoint of AQ.

10. In $\triangle ABC$, let O be the intersection of the perpendicular bisectors of sides AB and BC. Prove that O is equidistant from A, B and C, and hence that O is the centre of a circle which passes through the three vertices of the triangle. (This is the *circumcircle* of the triangle and O is the *circumcentre*.)

    Under what circumstances is O inside, outside or on the side of $\triangle ABC$?

11. Two lines m and n meet at right angles, and X and Y are two points on m and n which move so that the length XY is constant. Find the locus of the midpoint of XY.

12. Q, R, S and T are fixed points. Find the locus of P such that the sum of the areas of $\triangle PQR$ and $\triangle PST$ is constant.

8.2   Constructions

According to the classical rules of Euclidean geometry, constructions are to be made with only a *straight edge* and a pair of *compasses*. It is worth taking a little time to describe what these tools are for.

Straight edge   A straight edge is a ruler without a graduated scale, so you cannot measure with it. You are allowed to draw a line through any two given points, and you are allowed to extend any line which is already drawn. In effect, therefore, lines are infinitely long.

Compasses   The compasses are for drawing circles. Strictly speaking, you are only permitted to draw a circle if you already have two points A and B; you are then allowed to draw a circle with centre at A which passes through B. This enables you to construct new points where two circles intersect.

Here is a simple example.

Constructing an equilateral triangle

Given two points A and B, one can construct a point C such that $\triangle ABC$ is equilateral.

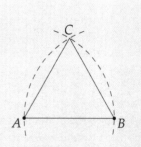

(i) Draw an arc centred at A through B.
(ii) Draw an arc centred at B through A.
(iii) Let C be the intersection of the two arcs.
(iv) Join A, B and C to create the triangle.

The rules mean that you are not allowed to 'transfer' a distance, in the sense of drawing a circle with a given point as centre whose radius is equal to the distance between two other points. As a consequence the compasses are 'floppy'; if you try to use them to move a distance PQ from one place to another, they will collapse and prevent you doing so. However, it can be proved that there *is* a way of transferring distances using floppy compasses.

Transferring a distance

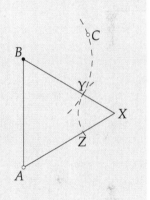

Given three points A, B and C, one can construct a circle with centre A and radius BC.

(i) Construct X so that $\triangle ABX$ is equilateral.

(ii) Draw an arc centred at B through C; let Y be the point where this arc meets BX.

(iii) Draw an arc centred at X through Y; let Z be the point where this arc meets XA.

(iv) Now $AZ = BC$.

It is now clear that, using this construction, you can transfer distances whenever you need to. Hence it is usual in school geometry to treat the compasses as if they were 'rigid'.

Problems 8b

1. Prove that the equilateral triangle construction works.

2. Prove that the method for transferring a distance works.

3. Given two points A and B, construct the perpendicular bisector of AB.

4. Given three points A, B and C which are not in a straight line, construct the bisector of $\angle ABC$.

5. Given three non-collinear points A, B, C and points O and X, construct a point Y so that $\angle YOX = \angle ABC$. (So angles can also be 'transferred'.)

6. Given a line m and a point A which is not on it, construct a line through A which is parallel to m.

7. Given a line m and a point A which is not on it, construct a line through A which is perpendicular to m.

8. Given a line m and a point A on it, construct a line through A which is perpendicular to m.

9. (a) Given a line AB and two points X and Y on the same side of AB, construct a point C on AB such that $\angle ACX = \angle BCY$.

    (b) Let P be any point on AB other than C. Prove that $XC + CY < XP + PY$.

10. Given a circle, with three points A, B and C on the circumference, show how to construct its centre.

11. Given $\triangle ABC$, construct an isosceles triangle, on base AB, which has the same area as $\triangle ABC$.

12. Given $\triangle ABC$, construct a triangle with a given altitude which has the same area as $\triangle ABC$.

13. Given $\triangle ABC$ and a point P on AB, construct a line through P which cuts the area of the triangle into two equal halves.

14. Given a quadrilateral $ABCD$ as shown, construct a point E on BA produced so that $[BEC] = [ABCD]$.

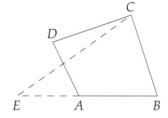

15. Points A and B are fixed, and a point P moves so that $PA^2 + PB^2$ is a constant. Find the locus of P.

16. Points A and B are fixed, and a point P moves so that $PA^2 - PB^2$ is a constant. Find the locus of P.

Chapter 9

Circles and tangents

9.1 Basic properties

A line and a circle in the same plane either meet at two points (in which case the line cuts off a chord on the circle), or at one point (in which case the line is a tangent to the circle), or they fail to meet at all.

Tangent and radius

(a) A line perpendicular to a radius at a point on a circle is a tangent.

(b) The tangent at a point on a circle is perpendicular to the corresponding radius.

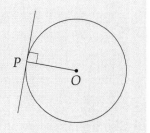

Tangents from an external point

The two tangents from an external
point to a circle are equal in length,
and the line from P to the centre of
the circle bisects the angle $T_1 P T_2$.

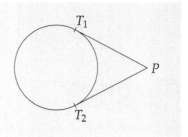

Problems 9a

1. Suppose P is on the circumference
   of a circle, and m is the line through
   P which is perpendicular to OP. Let
   A be any point on m.

   (a) Show that $OA > OP$ and so A
       lies outside the circle.

   (b) Show that m is a tangent.

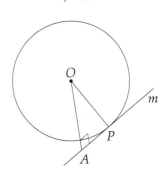

2. Suppose that m is the tangent to the
   circle at the point P. If $\angle OPA$ is not
   a right angle, let A be the foot of the
   perpendicular from O to m.

   (a) Show that $OA < OP$ and so A
       lies inside the circle.

   (b) Show that if PA is extended, it
       will cut the circle again.

   (c) What follows?

3. Let two circles, with centres A and B, touch each other at P. (This
   means that they share a common tangent at P.) Prove that the three
   points A, B and P are collinear. (There are two possible diagrams.)

4. Prove the theorem that tangents to a circle from a point are equal.

5. P is a point external to a circle with centre O, and PA, PB are tangents. Prove that OP bisects AB at right angles.

6. Prove that the diameter AB of a circle bisects all chords which are parallel to the tangents at A and B.

7. Given a circle and a point P outside it, show how to construct the tangents from P to the circle.

8. In $\triangle ABC$, let I be the intersection of the bisectors of $\angle ABC$ and $\angle ACB$. Prove that the perpendiculars from I to the three sides of the triangle are all equal, and hence that I is the centre of a circle which is tangential to all three sides. (This is the *incircle* of the triangle.)

   Show also that I lies on the bisector of $\angle CAB$. The point I is known as the *incentre* of the triangle.

9. In $\triangle ABC$, let I_1 be the intersection of the external bisectors of $\angle ABC$ and $\angle ACB$. Prove that the perpendiculars from I_1 to the three sides of the triangle are all equal, and hence that I_1 is the centre of a circle which is tangential to BC, AC produced and AB produced. (This is an *excircle* of the triangle.)

   Show also that I_1 lies on the internal bisector of $\angle BAC$. The point I_1 is known as an *excentre* of the triangle; there are two other such excentres.

Problems 9b

These problems involve calculations using the properties of tangents. It is often useful to add the centres to various circles and use Pythagoras' theorem.

1. The shaded semicircle is inscribed in an isosceles right-angled triangle, with equal sides of length 1.

   What is the radius of the semicircle?

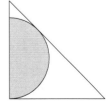

2. In the diagram, AB, CB and XY are tangents to the circle with centre O, and $\angle ABC = x$.

Find, in terms of x, the size of $\angle XOY$.

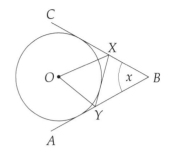

3. $\triangle AOB$ is an isosceles right-angled triangle drawn in a quadrant of a circle of radius 1. The largest possible circle, which has radius r, is drawn in the minor segment cut off by AB. The radius of the inscribed circle of AOB is R.

What is the ratio $R : r$?

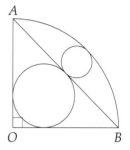

4. Two circles with radii 1 and 4 touch, as shown in the diagram. The line PQ is a tangent to both circles.

Find the length of PQ.

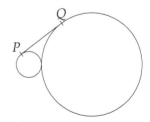

5. $\triangle PQR$ is right-angled at P, with $PQ = 15$ and $QR = 17$. Circular arcs are drawn with centres at P, Q and R, each arc touching the other two.

What is the radius of the arc centred at R?

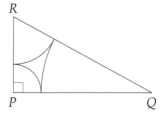

6. Circles with radii r and R (where $r < R$) touch each other and also touch two perpendicular lines, as shown.

What is the ratio $R : r$?

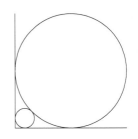

7. Three circles touch, as shown in the diagram. The two larger circles have radius 1 and the smaller circle has radius $\sqrt{2} - 1$.

What is the perimeter of the shaded region?

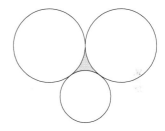

8. The diagram shows two circles of radius 105 which are tangent to each other and to a circle of radius 14.

What is the radius of the largest circle which can be placed in the shaded region?

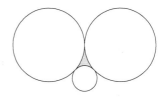

9. AB and CD are two parallel tangents to a circle, and BD is a third tangent.

Prove that $\angle BOD$ is a right angle.

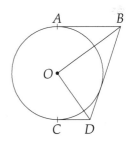

10. An equilateral triangle, of side a, is inscribed in a circle, as shown. Another equilateral triangle, of side b, is drawn in one of the segments so that the final diagram has a line of symmetry.

What is the ratio of $a : b$?

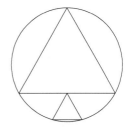

11. The diagram shows two parallel
    lines and three circles, which are
    tangential as illustrated. Circles C_1
    and C_2 have radius s and t
    respectively.

    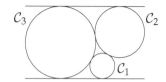

    What is the radius of circle C_3?

12. Two lines intersect at P. What is the locus of the centre of circles
    which are tangent to both lines?

13. Suppose that a polygon of perimeter p circumscribes a circle of
    radius r. Show that the area of the polygon is $\frac{1}{2}pr$.

14. Let AOB be a diameter of a circle centre O, and let C be any other
    point on the circle. Suppose that OE is a line parallel to AC, cutting
    the tangent at C at E. Prove that EB is a tangent to the circle.

15. Let AOB be a diameter of a circle centre O, and let C be any other
    point on the circle. The line AC, produced if necessary, meets the
    diameter perpendicular to AOB at D, and the line through D parallel
    to AOB meets the tangent at B at E. Prove that EC is a tangent to
    the circle.

16. $ABCD$ is an inscribable quadrilateral. Prove that $AB + CD = AD + BC$.

17. Prove that an inscribable parallelogram is a rhombus.

18. $ABCD$ is a quadrilateral such that $AB + CD = AD + BC$. Prove that
    it is inscribable.

19. The diagram shows two concentric
    circles. The lines AB and AC are
    tangential to the inner circle at X
    and Y.

    Prove that $BC = 2XY$.

    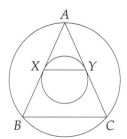

20. The pairs of tangents from the centres O_1 and O_2 of the two circles cut the circles at P, Q, R and S, as shown.

Prove that $PQ = RS$.

This result is sometimes called the *eyeball theorem*.

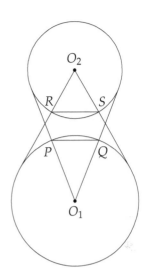

21. $\triangle ABC$ is equilateral and X, Y are the midpoints of AB and CA. The line XY, when produced, meets the circumcircle at Z.

Find the ratio $XY : YZ$.

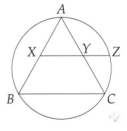

9.2   Tangents and angles

Alternate segment theorem

(a) If A, B and C are points on a circle, and AT is the tangent at A, with T and B on opposite sides of AC, then
$\angle ABC = \angle TAC$

(b) If T and B are points on opposite sides of AC, and $\angle ABC = \angle TAC$, then AT is a tangent to the circle through A, B and C.

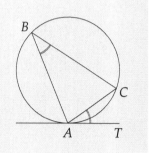

Problems 9c

1. Let AT be a tangent, AC a chord, and B a point in the alternate segment to angle CAT. Draw the diameter AOD.

   (a) Show that $\angle ADC = \angle TAC$.

   (b) Prove the alternate segment theorem.

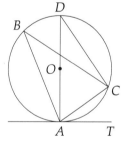

2. Let A, B, C and T be four points such that $\angle ABC = \angle TAC$. Draw the circumcircle of $\triangle ABC$.

   (a) Draw the diameter AD, and show that
   $\angle DAC + \angle ABC = 90°$.

   (b) Hence show that AT is a tangent to the circle.

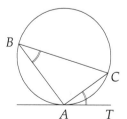

3. In the diagram, PQ and RS are tangents to the circle and QR meets the circle at T. The angles $\angle PTQ$, $\angle PQR$, $\angle QRS$ and $\angle SPT$ are denoted by a, b, c and x respectively.

   What is the value of x in terms of a, b and c?

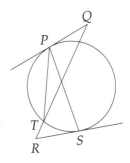

4. In the diagram, PQ is a tangent at N to the circle through L, M and N. The lengths LM and LN are equal, and LM produced meets the tangent PQ at the point R.

   If $\angle PNL = \theta$, what is the value of $\angle LRP$?

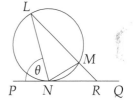

5. Two circles touch at A, and PAQ, RAS are two lines meeting the respective circles at P, R and Q, S. Prove that PR is parallel to QS.

6. Two circles meet at P and Q, and A is a point on one of the circles. The lines AP and AQ meet the other circle at R and S. Prove that RS is parallel to the tangent at A.

7. AOX is the diameter of a circle, and B is any other point on the circle. The point Y is the foot of the perpendicular from A to the tangent at B. Prove that AB is the bisector of $\angle YAX$.

8. $ABCD$ is cyclic, and AC and BD meet at X. Prove that CD is parallel to the tangent to the circumcircle of AXB at X.

9. $ABCD$ is cyclic, and E is a point on BA (produced if necessary) such that DE is parallel to CB. Prove the circumcircle of $\triangle DAE$ touches DC.

10. ABC is inscribed in a circle, and a line through B parallel to the tangent at A meets AC at D. Prove that the circumcircle of $\triangle BDC$ touches AB at B.

11. Two circles meet at P and Q. The tangent to the first circle at P meets the second circle again at R, and the tangent to the second circle at Q meets the first circle again at S. Prove that PS is parallel to QR.

12. Two equal circles meet at P and Q, and S is a point on one circle so that SQ is equal to QP. Show that SP is a tangent to the second circle.

13. AB and AC are equal chords of a circle, and P is any point on the chord BC. If AP meets the circle again at Q, prove that AB and AC are tangents to the circumcircles of $\triangle BPQ$ and $\triangle CPQ$ respectively.

14. AB is a diameter of a circle and C and D are two points on the circle. The chords AC and AD, when produced, meet the tangent at B at P and Q. Prove that the circumcircles of $\triangle BCP$ and $\triangle BDQ$ are tangential at B.

9.3   Common tangents

A line which touches two circles is called a common tangent; in general, there are four such tangents to two circles. If the circles lie on the same side of a common tangent, it is a *direct common tangent*, and if they lie on opposite sides, it is a *transverse common tangent*. In order for the former to exist, it is sufficient that neither circle lies within the other; for the latter, we need the two circles to lie entirely outside each other. We shall also assume that one circle is larger than the other, since the case when they are equal is easy to deal with. Let the larger circle have centre O_1 and radius r_1, and the smaller centre O_2 and radius r_2, and let $d = r_1 - r_2$ and $s = r_1 + r_2$.

Construction of direct common tangents

Draw a circle, centre O_1 and radius d.
Construct a tangent from O_2 to this circle,
touching it at S.

Let O_1S meet the larger circle at T.
Construct the tangent at T, meeting the
line of centres at C_e.

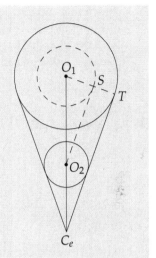

Construction of transverse common tangents

Draw a circle, centre O_1 and radius s.
Construct a tangent from O_2 to this circle,
touching it at S.

Let O_1S meet the larger circle at T.
Construct the tangent at T, meeting the
line of centres at C_i.

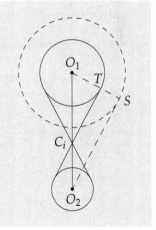

The points C_e and C_i are known as the *external* and *internal centres of
similitude* of the two circles.

Problems 9d

1. Prove that the two constructions work, and show how to adapt them if the circles are of equal radius. Find formulae, in terms of r_1, r_2 and the distance between the centres, for the lengths cut off by each tangent between the points of contact.

2. Two circles touch externally at the point A. If a direct common tangent touches the circles at P and Q, prove that PA and QA are perpendicular.

3. Prove that
$$\frac{O_1 C_i}{C_i O_2} = \frac{r_1}{r_2} = \frac{O_1 C_e}{C_e O_2}.$$
We say that C_i and C_e *divide* $O_1 O_2$ *internally* and *externally* in the ratio $r_1 : r_2$.

4. Let P be any point on the circle with diameter $C_i C_e$. Prove that the two centres of similitude lie on the internal and external bisectors of $\angle O_1 P O_2$.

5. Two circles meet at P and Q. A common tangent touches the circles at A and B. The chord AP meets BQ at X and BP meets AQ at Y. Prove that $\angle YXQ$ is equal to $\angle YPQ$.

6. Two intersecting circles C_1 and C_2 have a common tangent which touches C_1 at P and C_2 at Q. The two circles intersect at M and N, where N is closer to PQ than M is. The line PN meets the circle C_2 again at R. Prove that MQ bisects $\angle PMR$.

7. Two touching circles C_1 and C_2 share a common tangent which meets C_1 at A and C_2 at B. Let AP be a diameter of C_1 and let the tangent from P to C_2 touch it at Q. Prove that $AP = PQ$.

Chapter 10

Circles: lengths and areas

10.1 Areas

Since all circles are similar, the ratio of the circumference to the diameter is constant, and, as everybody knows, this ratio is π. Hence the circumference of a circle of radius r is $2\pi r$.

Area of a circle

The area of a circle of radius r is πr^2.

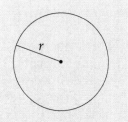

Problems 10a

1. (a) Divide a circle up into a very large number of very small sectors. Rearrange these sectors as shown by placing them alternately 'up' and 'down'.

    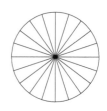

    Approximating this figure by a parallelogram, state its dimensions.

    Allowing the number of sectors to become infinite, prove that the area of the circle is πr^2.

    (b) As an alternative to this argument, use the result of Problems 9b question 13, on page 84.

2. O is the centre of a circle of radius 1, with radii OA and OC, and $OABC$ is a square.

    Find the shaded area.

    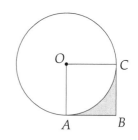

3. The diagram shows three semicircles, each of radius 1.

    Find the total shaded area.

    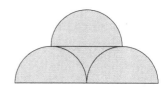

4. The figure is made up of a straight line of length 16 and two quarter circles, one with centre at the midpoint of the line.

    Find the area of the figure.

    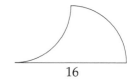

5. The diagram shows a semicircle containing a circle, which touches its circumference and diameter.

What fraction of the semicircle is shaded?

6. The diagram shows two semicircular arcs, *PQRS* and *QOR*. The diameters, *PS* and *QR*, of the two semicircles are parallel. The line *PS* has length 4 and is a tangent to semicircular arc *QOR*.

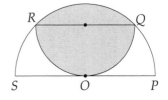

What is the area of the shaded region?

7. The diagram shows two concentric circles of radii 1 and 2 and some sectors defined by an angle of 120° at the centre.

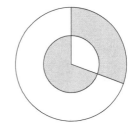

What is the ratio of the total shaded area to the total unshaded area?

8. The smaller circle touches the larger circle and goes through its centre.

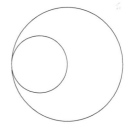

What fraction of the area of the larger circle is outside the smaller circle?

9. The diagram shows seven circles of equal radius which fit snugly inside the larger circle.

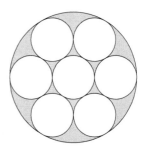

What is the ratio of the unshaded area to the shaded area?

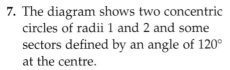

10. The diagram shows two concentric
circles; the inner has radius b and
the other has radius c. The points P
and Q lie on the two circles, and PQ
is tangential to the inner circle.

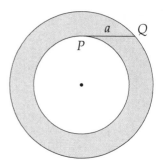

(a) Allow P to move around the
    inner circle. The line segment
    PQ sweeps out the area of the
    annular ring between the
    circles. Show that the area of
    this annulus is $\pi(c^2 - b^2)$.

(b) However, the same area would
    be swept out if the point P were
    kept at rest and the tangent
    allowed to rotate. Use this idea
    to prove Pythagoras' theorem.

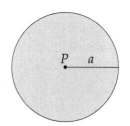

11. AB is a diameter of a circle of
radius 1. Two circular arcs of equal
radius are drawn with centres A and
B, and meet on the circle, as shown.

What is the total shaded area?

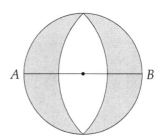

12. The diagram shows a square with its
circumcircle and four semicircles
constructed externally on the sides
of the square.

If the radius of the circumcircle is 1,
find the total shaded area.

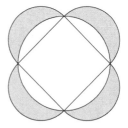

13. The area of each semicircle is 2.

What is the difference between the areas of the black and grey shaded regions?

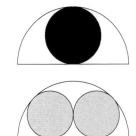

14. The diagram shows four touching circles, each of which also touches the sides of an equilateral triangle of side length 3.

What is the shaded area?

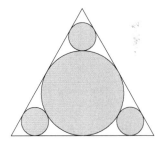

15. A company logo has a centrally-symmetric white cross of width $\sqrt{2}$ on a dark circle. The dark corner pieces have sides of length 1 as shown.

What is the total shaded area?

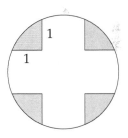

16. The diagram shows the design for a leaded window. The two pairs of parallel lines divide the circle of radius 1 into nine pieces in such a way that all the arcs are equal.

Find the area of each piece.

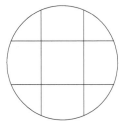

17. The three-petal lotus shown in the diagram is formed by three arcs, each of radius 1, the radius of the circle.

What is the area of the shaded region?

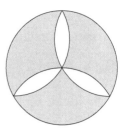

10.2   Rectangle properties

Intersecting chords—inside the circle

If two chords AB and CD of a circle meet at a point X inside the circle, then

$$AX \times BX = CX \times DX.$$

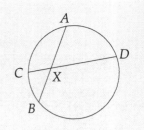

Intersecting chords—outside the circle

If two chords AB and CD of a circle meet at a point X outside the circle, then

$$AX \times BX = CX \times DX.$$

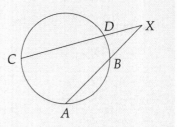

Intersecting chord and tangent

If a chord AB of a circle and the tangent at a point T meet at a point X outside the circle, then

$$AX \times BX = TX^2.$$

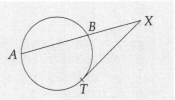

The first two of the results above are sometimes known as the *rectangle properties*, since they can be thought of as referring to the areas of rectangles whose sides are equal to the chord segments. The third is often called the *tangent secant theorem*.

Problems 10b

1. Prove the results about intersecting chords, by joining AD and BC and showing that $\triangle AXD \sim \triangle BXC$. For the tangent-secant theorem, join AT and BT.

2. $\triangle ABC$ is right-angled at A, and D is the foot of the altitude from A to BC. Prove that $BD \times DC = AD^2$.

3. The diagram shows a triangle with a chord AY which is perpendicular to a diameter. Let $AO = a$, $AY = b$ and $OY = c$.

   Use intersecting chords to prove Pythagoras' theorem.

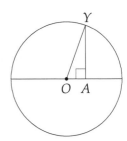

4. $\triangle ABC$ is right-angled at C, and CD is an altitude. The circumcircles of $\triangle ADC$ and $\triangle BDC$ are drawn.

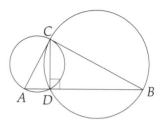

Show that AC is a tangent to the circumcircle of $\triangle BDC$ and that BC is a tangent to the circumcircle of $\triangle ADC$, and use tangent-secant to prove Pythagoras' theorem.

5. $\triangle AOB$ is right-angled at O, and X is a point on AB so that $OX = OA$. Prove that $AX \times AB = 2 \times AO^2$.

6. AB is a diameter of a circle, and ℓ is any line perpendicular to AB. If X is a variable point on the circle, and Y is the point where AX meets ℓ, prove that $AX \times AY$ is a constant.

7. AB is a diameter of a circle, and X is a point outside the circle. A line through X intersects the circle at C and D, and XP is the perpendicular from X to AB, possibly produced. Prove that

$$XP^2 = XC \times XD \pm AP \times PB,$$

where the $+$ sign is taken if P is inside the circle, and the $-$ sign if P is outside.

8. $\triangle ABC$ is equilateral and D an internal point of the side BC. A circle, tangent to BC at D, cuts AB internally at M and N, and AC internally at P and Q. Prove that $BD + AM + AN = CD + AP + AQ$.

9. Two circles C_1 and C_2 intersect at M and N, and have a common tangent which touches C_1 at P and C_2 at Q.

   (a) Show that MN bisects PQ.

   (b) Prove that $\triangle MNP$ and $\triangle MNQ$ have equal areas.

10. The diagram shows two circles which meet at A and B. The direct common tangents are PQ and RS.

Prove that $XY^2 - AB^2 = PQ^2$.

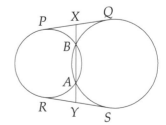

11. $\triangle ABC_1$ and $\triangle ABC_2$ have $AB = c$ and $AC_1 = AC_2 = b$ as well as the same angle at B.

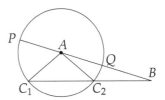

(a) Show that $BC_1 \times BC_2 = c^2 - b^2$ and $BC_1 + BC_2 = 2c \cos B$.

(b) Form a quadratic equation in a with roots BC_1 and BC_2.

(c) Comment — relating this to the ambiguous case.

12. Three circles C_1, C_2 and C_3 intersect as follows: circles C_1 and C_2 intersect at A and B; circles C_2 and C_3 intersect at C and D; circles C_3 and C_1 intersect at E and F. Prove that the three lines AB, CD and EF are concurrent.

13. Two circles meet at A and B. Find the locus of a point P which moves so that the tangents to the two circles are equal.

14. Let $\triangle ABC$ be acute-angled, and construct semicircles outwardly on the sides BC and CA. Let the altitudes AD and BE meet these semicircles at P and Q. Prove that $CP = CQ$.

15. XY is a diameter of a circle with centre O and G is a point on the diameter between X and Y. The perpendicular to XOY at G meets the circle at Z, the point H is on OZ such that the line GH is perpendicular to OZ, and OP is both parallel to HG and equal in length to OG. If $XG = a$ and $GY = b$, find, in terms of a and b, the lengths of ZH, ZG, ZO and ZP.

If $a \neq b$, deduce that

$$\frac{2ab}{a+b} < \sqrt{ab} < \frac{a+b}{2} < \sqrt{\frac{a^2+b^2}{2}}.$$

What happens if $a = b$?

Converse results

If two lines AXB and CXD are such that $AX \times BX = CX \times DX$, then $ADBC$ is cyclic.

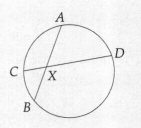

If two lines ABX and CDX are such that $AX \times BX = CX \times DX$, then $ABDC$ is cyclic.

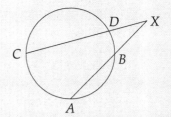

If two lines ABX and TX are such that $AX \times BX = TX^2$, then XT is a tangent to the circumcircle of $\triangle ABT$.

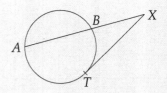

Problems 10c

1. Use proof by contradiction to show the converse results. For example, assume that the point D does not lie on the circumcircle of $\triangle ABC$ and show that a contradiction follows.

2. Two circles C_1 and C_2 intersect. The chords AB of C_1 and CD of C_2 intersect at X on the common chord of the two circles. Prove that A, B, C and D are concyclic.

3. Let AB be a fixed line segment, and let C be a point on the line through B perpendicular to AB. Let P be the point on AC such that $AP \times AC = AB^2$; find the locus of P as C varies.

4. Let AT be a tangent from a point A to a circle, and let M be the midpoint of AT. A variable line through M cuts the circle at X and Y. Prove that the centre of the circumcircle of $\triangle AXY$ lies on a fixed line, which should be identified.

10.3   Ptolemy's theorem

If $ABCD$ is a cyclic quadrilateral, then

$$BC \times AD + CD \times AB = AC \times BD.$$

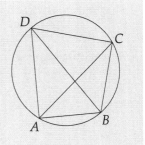

If $ABCD$ is not cyclic, the result becomes an inequality, as in question 9 of Problems 10d.

Problems 10d

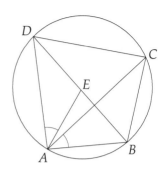

1. Let E be the point on BD such that $\angle DAE = \angle BAC$.

   (a) Prove that $\triangle DAE \sim \triangle CAB$ and that $\triangle BAE \sim \triangle CAD$.

   (b) Hence show that

   $$BC \times AD = AC \times DE$$
   $$\text{and} \quad CD \times AB = AC \times BE.$$

   (c) Add these equations to prove Ptolemy's theorem.

2. Apply Ptolemy's theorem to a rectangle to produce a proof of Pythagoras' theorem.

3. $\triangle ABC$ is isosceles with $AB = AC$. From B and C, lines BX and CY are drawn, perpendicular to AB and AC and meeting at D. Prove that $BC \times AD = 2 \times AB \times DX$.

4. $\triangle ABC$ is an equilateral triangle inscribed in a circle, and P is any point on the minor arc BC. Prove that $PA = PB + PC$.

5. A regular hexagon $ABCDEF$ is inscribed in a circle. If P is on the minor arc BC, show that $PA + PB + PC + PD = PE + PF$.

6. A square $ABCD$ is inscribed in a circle, and P lies on the minor arc AB. Prove that $PA + PC = \sqrt{2} \times PD$.

7. A regular pentagon has side length a and the diagonal has length d. Prove that $d^2 - ad - a^2 = 0$ and hence that

   $$d = \left(\tfrac{1+\sqrt{5}}{2} \right) a.$$

8. A regular pentagon $ABCDE$ is inscribed in a circle. If P is on the minor arc AB, prove that $PA + PB + PD = PC + PE$.

9. Let $ABCD$ be any quadrilateral and let E be the point such that $\angle EAD = \angle BAC$ and $\angle ADE = \angle ACB$.

(a) Prove that $\triangle ABC \sim \triangle AED$.

(b) Prove that $\triangle ABE \sim \triangle ACD$.

(c) Deduce that

$$AD \times BC = AC \times ED$$

and $$AB \times CD = AC \times BE.$$

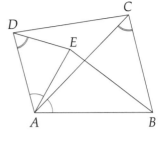

(d) Add these to conclude that

$$AB \times CD + AD \times BC \geq AC \times BD$$

with equality if, and only if, $ABCD$ is cyclic.

10.4 Apollonius circles

Let A and B be fixed points, and let λ be a constant, not equal to 1.

The locus of points P such that

$$\frac{PA}{PB} = \lambda$$

is a circle, the so-called *Apollonius circle*.

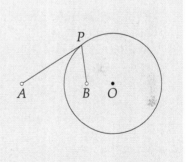

Problems 10e

1. Let A, B and λ be as above, and P a point on the locus.

(a) Let X, Y divide AB internally and externally in the ratio $\lambda : 1$. Prove that PX and PY are the internal and external bisectors of $\angle APB$.

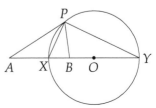

(b) Show that $\angle XPY$ is $90°$.

(c) Prove that the locus of P is a circle as claimed. Why is the case $\lambda = 1$ excluded in the definition above?

2. With the diagram of question 1, let $AX = \lambda$ and $XB = 1$, and find an expression for the length BY. Show that

$$\frac{YA}{YB} = \frac{AX}{BX}$$

and hence that the circle with diameter AB is also an Apollonius circle.

3. The diagram shows two circles with their external and internal centres of similitude.

Show that

$$\frac{O_1 C_i}{C_i O_2} = \frac{O_1 C_e}{C_e O_2}.$$

It follows that the circles on diameters $O_1 O_2$ and $C_i C_e$ form an Apollonius pair — what is the ratio λ?

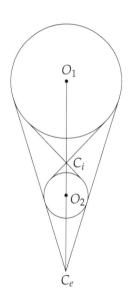

4. A, B and C are fixed collinear points, and P is a point such that $\angle APB + \angle APC = 180°$. Prove that the locus of P is a circle.

5. A and B are fixed points, and ℓ is a line parallel to AB at distance AB from it. Determine the position of a point P on ℓ such that $AP : PB$ is a maximum.

Chapter 11

Triangle centres

In this chapter we will look at the so-called *triangle centres*. These include several points which are the intersections of concurrent lines. Three have already been met, but we introduce some others. One of the purposes of this work is to investigate the relationships between the centres.

11.1   The Euler line

In this section, we prove the existence of a straight line containing three important triangle centres.

Circumcentre

The perpendicular bisectors of the sides are concurrent at the *circumcentre*, which is the centre of the *circumcircle*.

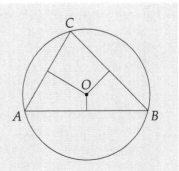

Orthocentre

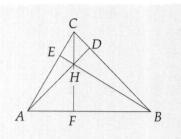

The altitudes are concurrent at the *orthocentre*.

Centroid

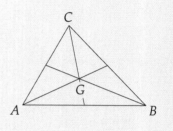

The medians are concurrent at the *centroid*.

It is worthwhile summarising some standard notation for triangles, not all of which you have yet met.

▷ The lengths of AB, BC and CA are c, a and b.
▷ The perimeter is $p = a + b + c$ and the semi-perimeter is $s = \frac{1}{2}p = \frac{1}{2}(a + b + c)$.
▷ The midpoints of AB, BC and CA are C_1, A_1 and B_1.
▷ The feet of the altitudes from A, B and C are D, E and F.
▷ The midpoints of AH, BH and CH are U, V and W, the *Euler points*.
▷ The circumcentre is O.
▷ The orthocentre is H.
▷ The centroid is G.
▷ The incentre is I and the excentres opposite A, B and C are I_A, I_B, I_C.
▷ The nine-point centre is N.
▷ The circumradius is R.
▷ The inradius is r and the exradii opposite A, B and C are r_A, r_B and r_C.

Problems 11a

1. It is worth returning to the sine rule. Draw the diameter through A.

   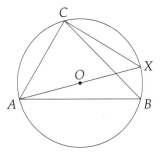

   (a) Prove that $\triangle AXC$ is right-angled, and hence that $b = AX \sin B$.

   (b) Deduce the sine rule in the form

   $$\frac{a}{\sin A} = \frac{b}{\sin B} = \frac{c}{\sin C} = 2R,$$

   where R is the circumradius.

2. Two fixed lines m and n intersect at A. Points B and C slide on m and n such that BC is of a constant length. Determine the locus of P, the circumcentre of $\triangle ABC$.

3. $\triangle ABC$ is isosceles with $AB = AC$. If X is any point on BC, and P and Q are the circumcentres of $\triangle ABX$ and $\triangle ACX$, prove that $APXQ$ is a rhombus.

4. Let A, B and C be points on a line (in that order), and let D be a point not on the line. Let the circumcentres of $\triangle ABD$, $\triangle BCD$ and $\triangle ACD$ be X, Y and Z. Prove that $\angle XDY = \angle ADC$, and hence that $XZYD$ is a cyclic quadrilateral.

5. The diagonals of a quadrilateral $ABCD$ meet at O, and the centres of the circumcircles of triangles $\triangle ABO$, $\triangle BCO$, $\triangle CDO$ and $\triangle DAO$ are P, Q, R and S. Prove that $PQRS$ is a parallelogram.

6. $ABCD$ is a cyclic quadrilateral, with AB and DC produced to meet at P and CB and DA produced to meet at Q. The circumcircles of $\triangle PBC$ and $\triangle QAB$ intersect at a second point R. Prove that P, R and Q are collinear.

7. Two circles, centred at O_1 and O_2, intersect at X and Y. The points A and B lie on the circles, AXB is a straight line, and C is the point where AO_1 and BO_2 intersect.

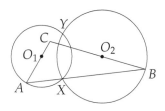

Prove that Y lies on the circumcircle of $\triangle CO_1O_2$.

8. $\triangle ABC$, where $AB < AC$, has circumcircle S. The perpendicular from A to BC meets S again at P. The point X lies on the line segment AC, and BX meets S again at Q. Prove that $BX = CX$ if, and only if, PQ is a diameter of S.

9. Identify the orthocentres of triangles $\triangle AHB$, $\triangle BHC$ and $\triangle CHA$.

10. Prove the following results.

   (a) $\angle AHE = \angle ACB$ (with similar results for each of the other angles around H).

   (b) The three triangles $\triangle AEF$, $\triangle DBF$ and $\triangle DEC$ are all similar to $\triangle ABC$.

   (c) DH, EH and FH are the angle bisectors of $\triangle DEF$ (and hence H is the incentre of $\triangle DEF$).

   (d) The angles of $\triangle DEF$ are $180° - 2A$, $180° - 2B$ and $180° - 2C$.

11. Prove that, if $\angle BAC$ is acute, then $\angle BHC = 180° - \angle BAC$. If BC and $\angle BAC$ are fixed, what is locus of H as A moves?

12. Prove that the perpendicular bisector of EF passes through A_1.

13. Two circles intersect at P and Q. A variable line through P meets the circles at A and B. Find the locus of the orthocentre of $\triangle ABQ$.

14. Let the two medians AA_1 and BB_1 intersect at G. Draw CC^* through G so that $CG = GC^*$, intersecting AB at C'.

(a) Prove that C^*B is parallel to GA_1.

(b) Prove that C^*A is parallel to GB_1.

(c) Prove that GAC^*B is a parallelogram.

(d) Prove that C' is the midpoint of AB, and hence that the medians are concurrent at G.

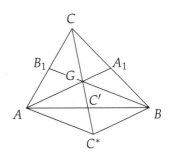

15. Prove the following results.

   (a) G is the point of trisection of each median.

   (b) The triangles $\triangle AC_1B_1$, $\triangle BA_1C_1$, $\triangle CA_1B_1$ and $\triangle A_1B_1C_1$ are congruent, and all similar to $\triangle ABC$.

   (c) The six triangles formed around G are all of equal area.

   (d) G is the centre of mass of $\triangle ABC$, thought of as a flat shape of uniform density (known as a *lamina*).

16. If $AG = BC$, prove that $\angle BGC = 90°$.

17. $\triangle ABC$ is a triangle with $AC > AB$. The point X lies on the side BA extended through A, and the point Y lies on the side CA in such a way that $BX = CA$ and $CY = BA$. The line XY meets the perpendicular bisector of side BC at P. Prove that $\angle BPC + \angle BAC = 180°$.

The Euler line

The points O, G and H are collinear and the ratio $OG : GH = 1 : 2$.

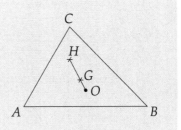

You will meet several proofs of the existence of this line.

Problems 11b

We begin by approaching the triangle and its centres from a slightly different perspective.

1. Start with the points O and G. We know that $GC = 2C_1G$ and that OC_1 is perpendicular to AB. Let X be the point on OG produced so that $GX = 2OG$.

   (a) Prove that $\triangle GOC_1 \sim \triangle GXC$.

   (b) Deduce that CX is parallel to OC_1 and hence perpendicular to AB.

   (c) Similarly AX and BX are perpendicular to BC and CA.

   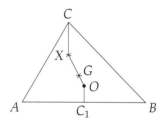

   (d) Hence X is the orthocentre H.

2. (a) Prove that $CH = 2OC_1$ (and similar results for BH and AH).

   (b) Prove that if AH is extended to meet the circumcircle at Y, then $HD = DY$.

3. (a) Prove that the triangles $\triangle HAB$, $\triangle HBC$ and $\triangle HCA$ all have circumradius R.

   (b) Prove that H is the circumcentre of the triangle whose vertices are the circumcentres of $\triangle HAB$, $\triangle HBC$ and $\triangle HCA$.

4. What is the Euler line of

   (a) an equilateral triangle?

   (b) an isosceles triangle?

   (c) a right-angled triangle?

5. Let $\triangle ABC$ be acute-angled with $AB > AC$ and $\angle BAC = 60°$. Suppose that the Euler line meets AB at P and AC at Q. Prove that $\triangle APQ$ is equilateral.

6. Three equal circles, centred at A, B and C, pass through a common point P. The other intersections are L (opposite A), M (opposite B) and N (opposite C). The point Q is the centroid of $\triangle LMN$, the point R is the centroid of $\triangle ABC$ and the point S is the circumcentre of $\triangle LMN$.

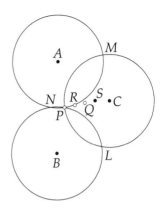

Show that P, Q, R and S are collinear and establish how they are spaced on the line.

11.2 The nine-point circle

It is a short step from here to prove one of the most celebrated results of triangle geometry.

The nine-point circle

There is a circle which passes through the following nine points:

A_1, B_1 and C_1;

D, E and F;

U, V and W.

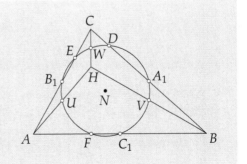

Here U, V and W are the midpoints of AH, BH and CH, the *Euler points*.

Problems 11c

1. Let U be the midpoint of AH, and let N be the intersection of A_1U and OH.

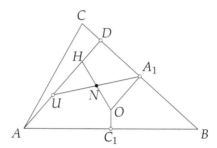

(a) Prove that UH is equal and parallel to OA_1.

(b) Hence show that $\triangle NOA_1$ and $\triangle NHU$ are congruent.

(c) Prove that N is the midpoint of OH and UA_1, and that D lies on the circle with diameter UA_1.

(d) Prove that this circle passes through the nine named points.

2. (a) Prove that the radius of the nine-point circle is $\frac{1}{2}R$.

(b) Prove that $OG : GN : NH = 2 : 1 : 3$.

(c) Prove that $OG : GN = OH : HN$.

(d) Prove that if $\angle BAC = 90°$, the nine-point circle passes through the vertex A.

(e) Prove that if $AB = AC$, the nine-point circle touches BC at A_1.

(f) Prove that the triangles $\triangle ABC$, $\triangle ABH$, $\triangle BCH$ and $\triangle CAH$ all have the same nine-point circle.

3. Prove that the nine-point circle of $\triangle AB_1C_1$ touches the nine-point circle of $\triangle A_1B_1C_1$.

4. Prove that the tangent to the nine-point circle at A_1 makes an angle of $|\angle C - \angle B|$ with BC.

11.3   The incentre and excentres

The internal bisectors of angles A, B and C are concurrent at the incentre I, which is the centre of a circle touching all three sides internally.

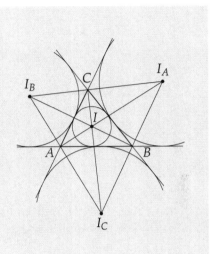

The internal bisector of angle A and the external bisectors of angles B and C are concurrent at the excentre I_A, which is the centre of a circle touching BC internally and AC and AB produced. Similarly there are excentres I_B and I_C.

Problems 11d

1. Suppose that the incircle touches the sides of $\triangle ABC$ at P, Q and R, and that the excircle opposite A touches the sides of $\triangle ABC$ at P_1, Q_1 and R_1, with similar notation for the other excircles.

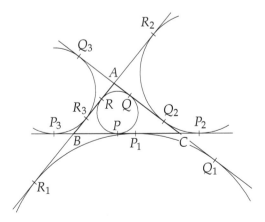

(a) Prove that

$$AQ = AR = s - a,$$
$$BR = BP = s - b,$$
$$\text{and} \quad CP = CQ = s - c.$$

(b) Prove that $AQ_1 = AR_1 = BR_2 = BP_2 = CP_3 = CQ_3 = s$.

(c) Prove that

$$BP_3 = BR_3 = CP_2 = CQ_2 = s - a,$$
$$AQ_3 = AR_3 = CQ_1 = CP_1 = s - b,$$
$$\text{and} \quad AQ_2 = AR_2 = BR_1 = BP_1 = s - c.$$

(d) Prove that the midpoints of BC, PP_1 and P_2P_3 are the same point, and similar results for the other two sides of $\triangle ABC$.

(e) Prove that

$$QQ_1 = RR_1 = a,$$
$$RR_2 = PP_2 = b,$$
$$\text{and} \quad PP_3 = QQ_3 = c.$$

2. (a) Prove that $rs = [ABC]$.

(b) Prove that $r_A(s - a) = [ABC]$.

(c) Prove that $\triangle I_A R_1 B \sim \triangle BRI$ and hence $rr_A = (s - b)(s - c)$.

Use parts (a), (b) and (c) to deduce *Heron's formula*

$$[ABC] = \sqrt{s(s - a)(s - b)(s - c)}.$$

3. Consider the incircle of $\triangle ABC$ which is right-angled at A.

(a) Prove that $r = s - a$.

(b) Express the area of $\triangle ABC$ in two different ways and hence prove Pythagoras' theorem.

4. Prove that, if $\angle BAC = 90°$, then $\angle BIC = 135°$.

5. Show how to construct three circles, centred at A, B and C, which touch in pairs on the sides of the triangle.

6. $ABCD$ is an inscribable quadrilateral. Prove that the incircles of $\triangle ABC$ and $\triangle ADC$ touch one another.

7. The incircle of $\triangle ABC$ touches BC at D. Prove that the incircles of $\triangle ABD$ and $\triangle ACD$ touch AD at the same point.

8. Let $ABCDEF$ be a hexagon (not necessarily regular) which circumscribes a circle S. The circle touches AB, CD and EF at their midpoints P, Q and R, respectively. Let X, Y and Z be the points of contact of S with BC, DE and FA, respectively. Prove that PY, QZ and RX are concurrent.

9. In $\triangle ABC$, $\angle BAC = 120°$. Let the angle bisectors of angles A, B and C meet the opposite sides at P, Q and R, respectively. Prove that the circle on diameter QR passes through P.

10. The altitudes AD, BE and CF meet the circumcircle at X, Y and Z. Prove that H is the incentre of triangle XYZ.

11. A triangle ABC has $AB > AC$. The internal bisector of $\angle BAC$ meets BC at P, the point Q is on AB such that $\angle QPB = 90°$, and R is a point on AC such that $\angle BQP = \angle PQR$. Prove that $\angle BAP = \angle RPC$.

11.4 Shifting the focus

Once you know the properties of the various triangle centres, it is sometimes possible to use these in a fruitful way to solve new problems. An unfamiliar diagram can often be 'reinterpreted' using a sort of 'change of perspective'.

For example, consider the diagram in the previous section, showing the incentre and excentres of a triangle $\triangle ABC$. If we shift our focus, so that $\triangle I_A I_B I_C$ becomes the 'basic' triangle, then we can see that $I_A A$, $I_B B$ and $I_C C$ are altitudes of this triangle, and it follows that they must meet in its orthocentre. But we know that they meet at the incentre I of the original $\triangle ABC$. Calling $\triangle I_A I_B I_C$ the *excentral triangle* of $\triangle ABC$, we now have the following result.

The incentre of a triangle is the orthocentre of its excentral triangle.

Problems 11e

1. Prove that H is the circumcentre of a triangle whose sides are the lines through A, B and C parallel to the opposite sides.

2. Prove that the circumcentre of a triangle is the nine-point centre of its excentral triangle.

3. Prove that O is the orthocentre of $\triangle A_1 B_1 C_1$ (which is known as the _medial triangle_ of $\triangle ABC$).

4. If $\triangle ABC$ is acute-angled, prove that the orthocentre H is the incentre of $\triangle DEF$. (This is known as the _orthic triangle_ of $\triangle ABC$.) Where are the excentres?

5. If $\triangle ABC$ is acute-angled, consider the triangle whose vertices are the circumcentres of triangles $\triangle OAB$, $\triangle OBC$ and $\triangle OCA$. Prove that O is the incentre of this triangle.

6. Consider the triangle whose vertices are the circumcentres of the triangles $\triangle IAB$, $\triangle IBC$ and $\triangle ICA$. Prove that I is the orthocentre of this triangle.

7. Consider the triangle formed by the circumcentres of the triangles $\triangle AB_1C_1$, $\triangle BC_1A_1$ and $\triangle CA_1B_1$. Prove that the orthocentre of this triangle is the circumcentre of the medial triangle of $\triangle ABC$.

8. Prove that the circumcircle of $\triangle ABC$ passes through the midpoint of $I_A I_B$.

9. Let K be the circumcentre of the excentral triangle of $\triangle ABC$. Prove that KI_A is perpendicular to BC.

11.5 The Simson line

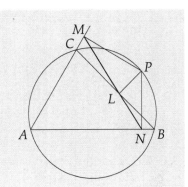

P is a point on its circumcircle of $\triangle ABC$. Perpendiculars PL, PM and PN are drawn to the sides BC, CA and AB, produced if necessary.

The points L, M and N are collinear.

The line so formed is called the *Simson line* or *pedal line* of P.

Problems 11f

1. Refer to the diagram above (but do not assume that LM and LN are part of the same straight line).

    (a) Prove that $\angle PCM = \angle PBN$.

    (b) Prove that $PMCL$ and $PLNB$ are cyclic.

    (c) Prove that $\angle CLM = \angle CPM = 90° - \angle PCM$.

    (d) Prove that $\angle BLN = \angle BPN = 90° - \angle PBN$.

    (e) Prove that L, M and N lie on a straight line.

2. Now consider the same diagram, but with the circumcircle omitted, and assume that LMN is a straight line.

    (a) Prove that $\angle MCP = \angle MLP$.

    (b) Prove that $\angle MLP = \angle PBN$.

    (c) Prove that P lies on the circumcircle of $\triangle ABC$.

3. Extend PN to meet the circumcircle at N'. Prove that the Simson line is parallel to CN', and hence, by symmetry, to AL' and BM'.

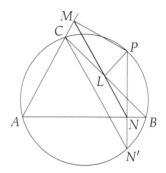

4. We relate the Simson line to the orthocentre H. Let CF meet the circumcircle again at F', and let PF' meet AB at C^*.

(a) Prove that PN' is parallel to CF'.

(b) Prove that $\angle N'CF' = \angle PF'C$.

(c) Prove that $\angle N'CF' = \angle C^*HF$.

(d) Prove that CN' is parallel to C^*H.

(e) Prove that the Simson line is parallel to C^*H.

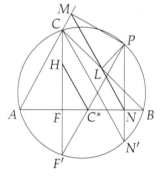

Now let HC^* and PN' (both produced) meet at X.

(f) Prove that $\triangle PNC^*$ and $\triangle XNC^*$ are congruent, and hence that $PN = NX$.

(g) Hence prove that the Simson line bisects PH.

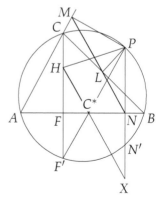

5. If the Simson line of P is parallel to CO, prove that PC is parallel to AB.

6. Let D' be the point where AD cuts the circumcircle. Prove that the Simson line of D' is the line through D parallel to the tangent at A to the circumcircle.

7. Let PQ be a chord of the circumcircle parallel to BC. Prove that the Simson line of P is perpendicular to AQ.

8. Prove that if P and Q are points at opposite ends of a diameter of the circumcircle of $\triangle ABC$, the Simson lines of P and Q meet at right angles on its nine-point circle.

11.6 Distances between centres

Euler's formula

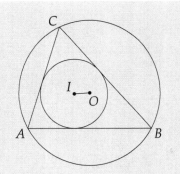

If O is the circumcentre and R the circumradius, I the incentre and r the inradius, then

$$OI^2 = R(R - 2r).$$

Problems 11g

1. Add to the diagram the line CIX, the diameters YX and PIQ and the line IZ which is perpendicular to AC.

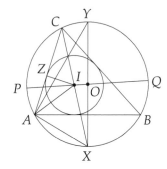

   (a) Prove that $\angle IAX = \frac{1}{2}(A+C)$.

   (b) Prove that $\angle AIX = \frac{1}{2}(A+C)$.

   (c) Prove that $AX = IX$.

   (d) Prove that $\triangle CZI \sim \triangle YAX$.

   (e) Prove that
   $$ZI \times YX = CI \times AX.$$

   (f) Prove that $2rR = CI \times IX$.

   (g) Prove that $PI \times IQ = R^2 - OI^2$.

   (h) Prove that Euler's formula is correct.

2. Prove that $2r \leq R$ and state the condition for equality.

3. Prove that
$$OH^2 = R^2(1 - 8\cos A \cos B \cos C)$$
and deduce the inequality
$$\cos A \cos B \cos C \leq \frac{1}{8}.$$

What are the conditions for equality?

Chapter 12

Collinearity and concurrency

As you have seen, some of the most interesting results in geometry describe surprising collinearities (the Euler line, the Simson line) or concurrencies (the triangle centres). In this chapter, we look at a number of alternative approaches.

12.1 Homothety

If $\triangle ABC$ and $\triangle A'B'C'$ are similar (so the angles are equal and the sides are in proportion) and, in addition, corresponding sides are parallel, we say the triangles are *homothetic*. To be precise, we would need to know that

$$\angle ABC = \angle A'B'C' \qquad AB \text{ is parallel to } A'B'$$
$$\angle BCA = \angle B'C'A' \qquad BC \text{ is parallel to } B'C'$$
$$\angle CAB = \angle C'A'B' \qquad CA \text{ is parallel to } C'A'$$

Centres of similitude

Two triangles are homothetic if, and only if, there is a centre of similitude.

This might be an external
centre (and the homothety
is direct) ...

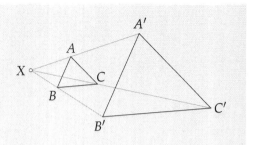

... or an internal centre
(and the homothety is
inverse) ...

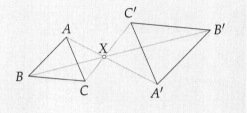

... and it could even be
inside the two triangles.
(This is a type of direct
homothety.)

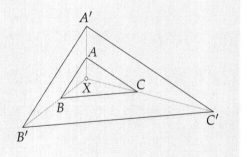

If the language of transformations is used, we call this an *enlargement* or
dilatation (not dilation!). In a direct homothety, the scale factor is positive,
and in an inverse homothety, it is negative. These results are easily proved
using similar triangles.

A particularly useful example of a direct homothety arises in connec-
tion with $\triangle ABC$ and its medial triangle $\triangle A_1B_1C_1$.

By the results of questions 14 and 15 of Problems 11a, $\triangle ABC$ and $\triangle A_1 B_1 C_1$ are inversely homothetic with centre of similitude G. Note that G is the centroid of both triangles, and that the scale factor from $\triangle A_1 B_1 C_1$ to $\triangle ABC$ is -2.

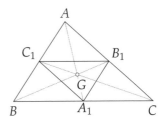

Once we have established an enlargement of this kind, it is possible to say that the enlargement maps any centre of one triangle to the corresponding centre of the other. This is a very fruitful idea, and it simplifies the treatment of the Euler line remarkably.

Problems 12a

The first five exercises explore the potential of this idea.

1. What is the orthocentre of the medial triangle? Prove that H, G and O are collinear, and that $GH = 2OG$, the Euler line property.

2. What is the circumcentre of the medial triangle? Prove that O, G and N are collinear, and that $OG = 2GN$.

3. Let S be the incentre of the medial triangle. Prove that I, G and S are collinear, and that $IG = 2GS$. (The point S is known as the *Spieker point* of $\triangle ABC$.)

4. Let $\triangle A_2 B_2 C_2$ be the triangle formed by drawing lines through A, B and C parallel to the opposite sides of $\triangle ABC$. This is known as the *anti-complementary triangle*. Prove that the orthocentre L of $\triangle A_2 B_2 C_2$ lies on the Euler line, and that $LG = 2GH$. (The point L is known as the *de Longchamps point* of $\triangle ABC$.)

5. Let K be the incentre of $\triangle A_2 B_2 C_2$ — it is known as the *Nagel point* of $\triangle ABC$. Prove that K is collinear with I, G and S, and that $KG = 2GI$.

6. Consider any two circles, centred at A and B. Let AX and BY be parallel radii (in the same direction) and let XY meet AB at Z.

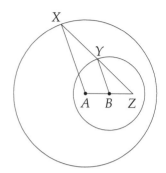

Prove that

$$\frac{ZY}{ZX} = \frac{YB}{XA} = k,$$

which is constant, and hence that Z is the (external) centre of similitude of the circles.

(This works equally well if the circles are disjoint or intersecting.)

7. Prove that a line joining H to any point on the circumcircle is bisected by the nine-point circle.

8. C_1 and C_2 are fixed non-intersecting circles, and K is a variable circle which touches them both externally.

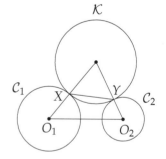

Prove that the line joining their points of contact X and Y passes through the external centre of similitude of C_1 and C_2.

9. Now let C_2 be entirely inside C_1 and let K be a variable circle which touches C_2 externally and C_1 internally. Prove that the line joining their points of contact passes through the internal centre of similitude of C_1 and C_2.

12.2   Ceva and Menelaus

Ceva's theorem and converse

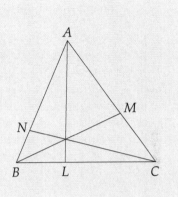

(a) If the lines AL, BM and CN are concurrent, then

$$\frac{BL}{LC} \times \frac{CM}{MA} \times \frac{AN}{NB} = 1.$$

(b) If

$$\frac{BL}{LC} \times \frac{CM}{MA} \times \frac{AN}{NB} = 1,$$

then the lines AL, BM and CN are concurrent.

The diagram shows the case when L, M and N are all internal to the sides. It is also possible, both in the theorem and the converse, to have one of the points internal to a side and the other two on the sides produced. In practice, it is often the converse form of Ceva's theorem which is particularly useful.

Problems 12b

1. Assume that AL, BM and CN meet at a point P inside the triangle; if they do not, the proof is easily adapted. Prove that

$$\frac{BL}{LC} = \frac{[BPA]}{[CPA]}$$

and hence prove Ceva's theorem.

2. Now assume that

$$\frac{BL}{LC} \times \frac{CM}{MA} \times \frac{AN}{NB} = 1.$$

Let BM and CN intersect at P, and produce AP to meet BC at L'. Use Ceva's theorem and conclude that L and L' are the same point.

3. Use Ceva's theorem to prove the concurrency of:

   (a) the medians;

   (b) the altitudes;

   (c) the internal angle bisectors.

4. Let X, Y and Z be the points of tangency of the incircle to the sides BC, CA and AB. Prove that AX, BY and CZ are concurrent. (The point of intersection is known as the *Gergonne point*.)

5. Equilateral triangles $\triangle CBX$, $\triangle ACY$, $\triangle BAZ$ are drawn outwardly on the sides of an acute-angled $\triangle ABC$. Prove that AX, BY and CZ are concurrent and equal in length. The point of intersection is known as the *Fermat point F*. Prove that the angles $\angle BFC$, $\angle CFA$ and $\angle AFB$ are all equal to $120°$.

6. Let AL, BM and CN be concurrent at P, and let L', M' and N' be the reflections of L, M and N in A_1, B_1 and C_1 respectively. Prove that AL', BN' and CM' are concurrent at P'. (Points P and P' thus related are called *isotomic conjugates*.)

7. Suppose that AL, BM and CN are concurrent, and that the circumcircle of $\triangle LMN$ intersects BC, CA and AB in points L', M' and N'. Prove that AL', BN' and CM' are concurrent.

8. In the standard Ceva diagram, prove that

$$\frac{PL}{AL} + \frac{PM}{BM} + \frac{PN}{CN} = 1.$$

9. In the standard Ceva diagram, prove that

$$\frac{AP}{PL} = \frac{AN}{NB} + \frac{AM}{MC}.$$

(This is sometimes called *van Aubel's theorem*.)

Menelaus' theorem and converse

(a) If a transversal meets the sides BC, CA and AB in L, M and N, then

$$\frac{BL}{LC} \times \frac{CM}{MA} \times \frac{AN}{NB} = 1.$$

(b) If

$$\frac{BL}{LC} \times \frac{CM}{MA} \times \frac{AN}{NB} = 1,$$

then the points L, M and N are collinear.

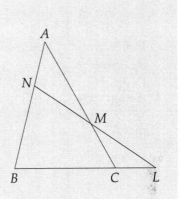

The diagram shows the transversal cutting two sides internally and one externally. It is also possible for the transversal to cut all three sides externally.

Problems 12c

1. Suppose that LMN is a transversal, as in the diagram. Draw CN' parallel to NM to cut AB at N'. Use similar triangles to express

$$\frac{BL}{LC} \quad \text{and} \quad \frac{CM}{MA}$$

in terms of lengths within AB, and hence prove Menelaus' theorem.

2. Suppose now that

$$\frac{BL}{LC} \times \frac{CM}{MA} \times \frac{AN}{NB} = 1.$$

Let N' be the point where LM meets AB. Prove that N' and N are the same point.

3. Let the tangent to the circumcircle at A meet CB produced at L. Prove that

$$\frac{BL}{LC} = \frac{c^2}{b^2}.$$

Hence prove that, if M and N are defined similarly, the points L, M and N are collinear.

4. A transversal cuts BC, CA and AB at L, M and N, and L', M' and N' are reflections of L, M and N in A_1, B_1 and C_1, respectively. Prove that L', M' and N' are collinear.

12.3   Centres of mass

Another line of attack uses the concept of centre of mass from statics. The basic idea is to hang different masses at appropriate points on the triangle and to calculate the position of the centre of mass in different ways. The result from mechanics which is needed is the following:

If masses m and n are placed at points A and B, they are equivalent to a single mass $m + n$ placed at the point C on AB, where $AC : CB = n : m$.

To see how to use this, place unit masses at the three vertices of a triangle ABC. The masses at B and C can be replaced by a mass of 2 at A_1, and now the masses at A and A_1 can be replaced by a mass of 3 at G_1, which divides AA_1 in the ratio $2 : 1$. But we could equally well have started with C and A and placed the single mass at G_2, which divides BB_1 in the ratio $2 : 1$, or with A and B and placed it at G_3, which divides CC_1 in the ratio $2 : 1$. Since these three centres of mass are the same point, the medians must be concurrent at a point which divides each of them in the ratio $2 : 1$.

Problems 12d

1. By considering masses of a, b and c placed at A, B and C, prove that the angle bisectors of $\triangle ABC$ are concurrent.

2. Let A, B, C, D, E and F be the midpoints of consecutive sides of a hexagon. Prove that $\triangle ACE$ and $\triangle BDF$ have the same centroid.

3. Prove that the lines joining each vertex of a triangle to the point where the incircle touches the opposite side are concurrent, by considering masses of $(s-b)(s-c)$, $(s-c)(s-a)$ and $(s-a)(s-b)$ placed at A, B and C.

4. Prove that the lines joining each vertex of a triangle to the point where the corresponding excircle touches the opposite side are concurrent at a point K, by considering masses of $b+c-a$, $c+a-b$ and $a+b-c$ placed at A, B and C.

5. Consider $\triangle ABC$ with masses of $b+c$, $c+a$ and $a+b$ placed at A, B and C. Show that the centre of mass is the same as that of masses of $2a$, $2b$ and $2c$ placed at A_1, B_1 and C_1, and hence is the incentre of the medial triangle of $\triangle ABC$, the Spieker centre. Alternatively, consider superimposing the situations of exercises 1 and 4, and hence prove that S is the midpoint of IK.

6. Prove Ceva's theorem using a centre of mass argument.

Chapter 13

Inversion

This final chapter introduces a very powerful method of proof, which has been described by one author as a mathematical 'dark art'.

13.1 Pole and polar

Inverse points

We are given a circle, centre O, and radius r. Two points P and Q which are collinear with O and for which $OP \times OQ = r^2$ are called *inverse points* with respect to the circle.

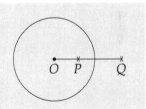

Pole and polar

If P and Q are inverse points with respect to a circle, the line through Q perpendicular to OP is called the *polar* of P, and P is called the *pole* of this line.

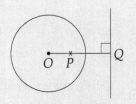

Reciprocal theorem

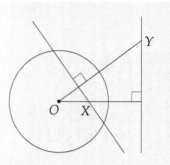

If the polar of X passes through Y,
then the polar of Y passes through X.

Problems 13a

1. Prove that

    (a) when P and Q are inverse points, if P is inside the circle, then Q is outside, and vice versa;

    (b) if P is on the circle, then it is its own inverse, and its polar is the tangent to the circle at P.

2. QT is a tangent to the circle centre O, and TP is perpendicular to OQ.

Prove that

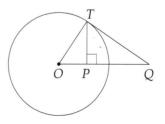

    (a) $\triangle OTQ \sim \triangle OPT$;

    (b) P and Q are inverse points;

    (c) P and T lie on the polar of Q.

(Thus, for a point outside the circle, the polar is the 'chord of contact'.)

3. Suppose that Y lies on the polar of X, with P inverse to X so that $OX \times OP = r^2$. Let Q be the foot of the perpendicular from X to OY.

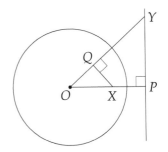

   (a) Prove that $QYPX$ is cyclic.

   (b) Prove that X lies on the polar of Y.

4. What happens in this proof

   (a) if X is outside the circle?

   (b) if Y lies on the circle?

   (c) if X lies on the circle?

5. Let P be a point outside a circle and let the tangents from P touch the circle at A and B. A line through P intersects the circle in points X and Y. Prove that the tangents at X and Y meet on the line AB. What happens if P is actually on the circle?

6. Let P be a point outside a circle and let the tangents from P touch the circle at A and B. Suppose that OP and AB meet at Q, and let XY be any chord through Q. If the tangents at X and Y meet at T, prove that PT is perpendicular to OP.

7. Suppose that the line p is the polar of P and the line q is the polar of Q. Prove that the line PQ is the polar of the point where p and q meet. What happens if p and q are parallel?

8. If Q lies on the polar of P, prove that the orthocentre H of $\triangle OPQ$ is the pole of PQ. Prove also that, in $\triangle PQH$, each vertex is the pole of the opposite side.

9. The incircle of $\triangle ABC$ touches the sides BC, CA and AB at P, Q and R. The line QR meets BC at X, the line RP meets CA at Y, and the line PQ meets AB at Z. Prove that X, Y and Z are collinear.

13.2   Harmonic ranges

If A, B, C, D are four collinear points such that

$$\frac{AC}{CB} = \frac{AD}{DB}$$

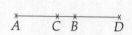

we say that they form a *harmonic range*.

Thus AB is divided internally at C and, in the same ratio, externally at D; this explains the order $ACBD$ on the line in the diagram.

It will be seen in the following exercise that this definition captures a theme familiar from many parts of geometry.

Problems 13b

1. Prove that the points O, G, N, H form a harmonic range on the Euler line.

2. Prove that the points I, G, S, K defined in questions 3 and 5 of Problems 12a (page 123) form a harmonic range.

3. In $\triangle ABC$, let the internal and external bisectors of $\angle BAC$ meet BC at P and Q. Prove that B, P, C, Q is a harmonic range.

4. Prove that, if C_i and C_e are the internal and external centres of similitude of two disjoint circles centred at O_1 and O_2, then O_1, C_i, O_2, C_e form a harmonic range.

5. Prove that the points A, X, B, Y defined in question 2 of Problems 10e (page 104), in the discussion of Apollonius circles, form a harmonic range.

6. Prove that if A, B, C, D is a harmonic range, then so is D, C, B, A.

7. If A, B, C, D is a harmonic range, and O is the midpoint of AB, prove that $OC \times OD = OB^2$.

8. If O is the midpoint of AB, and C, D are two points on AB such that $OC \times OD = OB^2$, prove that A, B, C, D is a harmonic range.

9. Let AP and AQ be tangents from a point A, outside a circle, to the circle, and let ABD be a chord intersecting the circle in B and D. Let C be the intersection of AD and PQ and let M be the midpoint of BD.

   (a) Prove that $APMQ$ is cyclic, and hence that $MC \times CA = PC \times CQ$.

   (b) Prove that $PC \times CQ = DC \times CB = MD^2 - MC^2$.

   (c) Prove that $MC \times CA = MD^2 - MC^2$ and hence $MC \times MA = MD^2$.

   (d) Prove that A, B, C, D is a harmonic range.

   (e) As the chord ABD varies (with A fixed), prove that the locus of points C which complete the harmonic range A, B, C, D is the polar of A.

10. Now let C be a fixed point inside a circle, and DCB a chord which is allowed to vary. Prove that the locus of points A which complete the harmonic range D, C, B, A is the polar of C.

11. Let A, B, C, D be a harmonic range and let m be a fixed line. Let A', B', C' and D' be the feet of the perpendiculars from A, B, C and D to m, in other words, the projections onto m. Prove that A', B', C', D' is also a harmonic range.

13.3   Properties of inversion

In principle, the technique of inversion is very simple. We start with a fixed circle Γ, called the *circle of inversion*, with centre O and radius r. As described above, any point P in the plane has an inverse point P^* with respect to Γ. As P traces out some figure (which is usually either a straight line or a circle), so does P^*. We call this figure the *inverse* (in the circle Γ) of the original one. It turns out that certain geometrical properties are conserved under this operation.

We state and prove certain fundamental properties of inversion.

A line through O inverts to itself.

The inverse of a line not through O is a circle through O.

The inverse of a circle through O is a line.

The inverse of a circle not through O is another circle not through O.

Inversion preserves 'angles of intersection' — in other words, two curves intersect at the same angle as do their inverses.

The first fact is very obvious, but note that the point O 'goes to infinity' under inversion. The second and third facts go together, since if P^* is the inverse of P, then P is the inverse of P^*. Note that the line turns out to be perpendicular to the diameter of the circle through O. The last two facts are a little more subtle. The final result is often used in problems about *orthogonal circles*, in which the tangents at the points of intersection are perpendicular.

All these results are proved in the next exercise, in which O is always the centre of inversion, and r is the radius of the circle of inversion. The circle Γ is omitted in the diagrams.

Problems 13c

1. Consider the line m not through O, and let A be the foot of the perpendicular from O. Let A^* be the inverse of A. Let P^* be the inverse of a point P on m.

   Show that P^* lies on the circle with diameter OA^*.

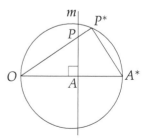

2. Conversely, begin with the circle through O on diameter OA^*. Let A be the inverse of A^*. Show that the inverse of this circle is the line m, through A and perpendicular to OA^*.

3. Let A be the centre of a circle to be inverted and let OT be the tangent from the centre of inversion, where $OT = t$. Let a line through O cut the circle at P and Q, and let P^* and Q^* be the respective inverses.

(a) Prove that $OP \times OQ = t^2$.

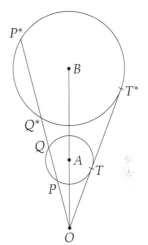

(b) Prove that $\dfrac{OP^*}{OQ} = \dfrac{r^2}{t^2}$.

(c) Prove that the locus of P^* is homothetic to that of Q, and hence another circle (with centre B).

(d) Prove that, if OT meets this locus at T^*, then it is a tangent and T^* is the inverse of T.

(e) Show that A and B are *not* inverse points with respect to Γ.

4. Show that the inverse of A with respect to Γ is the inverse of O with respect to the circle with centre B.

5. Let Q and R be collinear with O, and let the inverses of P, Q and R be P^*, Q^* and R^*.

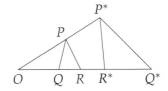

(a) Prove that PP^*Q^*Q and PP^*R^*R are cyclic.

(b) Prove that $\angle QPR = \angle Q^*P^*R$.

6. Now let P and Q be nearby points on one curve and P and R be nearby points on another curve, so that the two curves intersect at P. By allowing Q and R to approach P, show that the angle between the tangents to the curves at P is preserved under inversion.

7. Under what circumstances does a circle invert to itself?

13.4   Proof by inversion

Suppose we have a configuration and we wish to prove some geometrical result about it. By choosing an appropriate circle Γ, we invert the whole of the configuration in Γ to produce a *new* configuration. If this configuration has certain geometrical properties (which are easy to establish), then it will follow that corresponding results are true for the original one. Thus, by working on an easy configuration, it is possible to prove results for a more challenging one. The skill is in choosing the right centre of inversion; in many (but not all!) proofs, the actual *radius* of the circle of inversion doesn't matter.

We prove the following result as an example of the power of this process.

Result *OAB and OAC are orthogonal circles which intersect at O and A. Then the circles ABC and OBC are also orthogonal.*

PROOF We invert the configuration (shown on the left-hand side below) in O. The diagram on the right-hand side shows the inverted configuration, and, as is normal, the same labels are used for corresponding points.

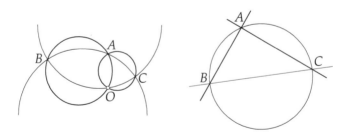

Circles OAB and OAC invert to straight lines. Since the circles are orthogonal, these lines meet at right angles at the image of A. The circle ABC inverts to a circle through the images of A, B and C, and the circle OBC inverts to the line through B and C. We must now prove that the line BC is orthogonal to the circle ABC. But the inverted configuration shows that BC is the diameter of the circle ABC, and it is clearly perpendicular to the tangents at the ends. This shows that the original circles are also orthogonal at B and C.   ❏

Problems 13d

It is intended that these questions are all answered by inversion: you may also like to try to find proofs by other methods.

1. Three circles OAB, OBC and OCA have a common point O, and their centres are X, Y and Z respectively.

If X lies on AO and Y on BO, prove that Z lies on CO.

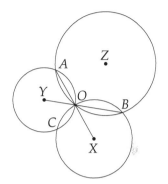

2. AB and CD are direct common tangents to two circles which intersect at O.

Prove that the circles ABO and CDO touch.

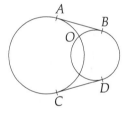

3. $OABC$ is a cyclic quadrilateral. A line through O cuts AB at X and CB at Y. Prove that the circumcircles of $\triangle OAX$ and $\triangle OCY$ touch.

4. A, B and C are points on a fixed line, and O is a point not on it. Prove that, if X, Y and Z are the circumcentres of $\triangle OAB$, $\triangle OBC$ and $\triangle OCA$, then the circumcircle of $\triangle XYZ$ passes through O.

5. Two circles C_1 and C_2 intersect orthogonally at P and a third circle C_3 touches them at Q and R. The point X is any point on this circle.

Prove that the circumcircles of $\triangle XPQ$ and $\triangle XPR$ intersect at $45°$.

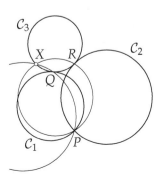

6. Three circles cut each other orthogonally at pairs of points A and A', B and B' and C and C'. Prove that the circumcircles of $\triangle ABC$ and $\triangle AB'C'$ touch at A.

7. Let $ABCD$ be a cyclic quadrilateral in a circle with centre O, and let P, Q, R and S be the circumcentres of $\triangle OAB$, $\triangle OBC$, $\triangle OCD$ and $\triangle ODA$. Prove that $\angle PBQ + \angle RDS = 180°$.

8. Two circles touch at O, and a line through O meets them at A and B. Prove that the tangents at A and B are parallel. (This is actually very easy without inversion, but what happens of interest when we do invert in O?)

13.5   Feuerbach's theorem

As a final flourish, we prove a wonderful theorem which relates the nine-point circle, the incircle and the three excircles of a triangle.

Feuerbach's theorem

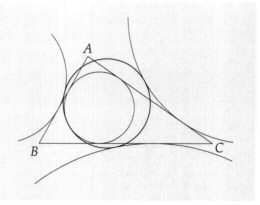

The nine-point circle touches the incircle and the three excircles.

Problems 13e

1. Let K and J be the points of contact on BC of the incircle and the excircle opposite A.

   Prove that the circle with diameter KJ has centre A_1.

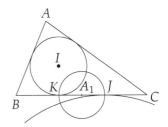

We are now going to invert the configuration with respect to this circle, which we will call Γ.

1. What is the angle between Γ and the incircle? What is the image of the incircle under inversion?

2. What happens to the excircle under inversion?

3. What happens to the line BC?

This leaves us with discovering the image of the nine-point circle. As this circle passes through the centre of inversion, it is a line, but we must find out which line it is, and that is the nub of the proof.

4. Show that this line passes through the image of D under the inversion.

5. Let the angle bisector at A cut BC at the point X. Recall from question 3 of Problems 13b that A, I, X, I_A is a harmonic range. Show that D, K, X, J is also harmonic. Hence find the image of D under the inversion.

6. Show that the image of the nine-point circle is a line through X parallel to the tangent to the nine-point circle at A_1, and that this makes an angle of $|\angle C - \angle B|$ with BC.

7. Let m be a line through X perpendicular to AX. Prove that the image of the nine-point circle is the reflection of BC in m.

8. Prove that this image is an transverse common tangent to the incircle and excircle.

To summarise, we now know that the inversion:

- takes the incircle to itself;
- takes the excircle to itself;
- takes the line BC to itself;
- takes the nine-point circle to the other transverse common tangent.

9. Prove Feuerbach's theorem.

Definitions

Notice that these are not given in alphabetical order. You will need to refer to these at various points in the book. Where appropriate, certain definitions have been listed as sub-definitions of others.

Angles

complementary angles two angles which add to 90°
supplementary angles two angles which add to 180°

Lines

line strictly speaking, a line through two points is infinitely long in both directions
line segment a line segment AB is the finite part of the line between the points A and B
ray a half-line — in other words, it has one endpoint and is infinite in the other direction

(In this book, we are not particularly rigorous about distinguishing between lines, rays and segments, since it is usually obvious from the context what is meant.)

produced if the segment AB is extended beyond B to a point C, it is said to produced to C
collinear three points which lie on the same line are collinear
concurrent three lines through the same point are concurrent
transversal a line which crosses two parallel lines is a transversal

Polygons

polygon	a closed figure made up of straight line segments.
	regular polygon a polygon with equal sides and equal angles
	pentagon a polygon with five sides
	hexagon a polygon with six sides
	heptagon a polygon with seven sides
	octagon a polygon with eight sides
	nonagon a polygon with nine sides
	decagon a polygon with ten sides
	dodecagon a polygon with twelve sides
vertex	a vertex is a corner of a polygon
diagonal	a line joining two non-adjacent vertices is a diagonal
convex	a polygon is convex if every diagonal lies inside it

If a circle can be drawn inside a polygon touching all of the sides, the polygon is an **inscribable polygon,** and if a circle can be drawn through all the vertices of a convex polygon, the polygon is a **circumscribable polygon.**

Triangles

triangle	a polygon with three sides
	scalene triangle a triangle whose three sides have different lengths
	isosceles triangle a triangle with two equal sides
	equilateral triangle a triangle with three equal sides
altitude	a line from a vertex perpendicular to the opposite side
orthocentre	the altitudes are concurrent at the orthocentre
median	a line from a vertex to the midpoint of the opposite side
centroid	the medians are concurrent at the centroid
angle bisector	a line which bisects the angle at a vertex
incentre	the internal angle bisectors are concurrent at the incentre
perpendicular bisector	a line through the midpoint of a side and perpendicular to that side
circumcentre	the perpendicular bisectors are concurrent at the circumcentre

Quadrilaterals

quadrilateral   a polygon with four sides

trapezium a quadrilateral with a pair of parallel sides

isosceles trapezium a trapezium whose non-parallel sides
  are equal

kite a quadrilateral with two pairs of adjacent sides equal

parallelogram a quadrilateral with two pairs of parallel
  sides

rectangle a parallelogram with a right angle

rhombus a parallelogram with two adjacent sides equal

square a rhombus with a right angle

Circles

In the diagrams, the two points A and B are on the circumference of a circle with centre O.

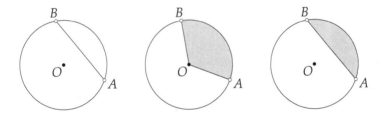

chord	the straight line segment joining A and B
arc	a curved portion of the circumference between A and B — the shorter of these is the **minor arc**, and the longer is the **major arc**
subtended	the angle $\angle AOB$ is subtended by AB at the centre O
minor sector	the region bounded by the lines AO and BO and the minor arc
major sector	the region bounded by the lines AO and BO and the major arc
minor segment	the region bounded by the chord AB and the minor arc
major segment	the region bounded by the chord AB and the major arc

Congruence

Two figures are **congruent** if they have precisely the same shape and size, but differ in position. By means of transformations, such as translations, rotations and reflections, one of the figures can be made to coincide with the other. If only the first two transformations are required, the figures are **directly congruent**; if one figure needs to be 'flipped over' (by reflection), they are **indirectly congruent**.

Notes, answers and hints

Chapter 1

Problems 1a

1. (c) This depends upon how carefully you state the result. Here is a possible converse.

   If $a + b + c + d + e = 360°$, then X and Y are the same point.

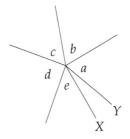

3. You need to consider different diagrams, depending on the order of the three lines.

4. (a) Yes, since it follows that $a + b = 180°$.

   (b) No, since we might have $a = 20°$, implying that $b = 160°$, and then BXD is clearly not a straight line.

   (c) This is true, and is a possible converse to the result about vertically opposite angles. Note, however, that it is not enough just to know that $a = c$.

Problems 1b

2. Draw a transversal crossing all three lines.

1.3   Angle sum of a polygon

The 'dynamic argument' to show the sum of the angles of a polygon is not rigorous, since it assumes a hidden use of the properties of parallel lines. To see why this is so, consider a triangle on a sphere with one vertex at the North Pole and the other two on the Equator at latitudes of 0° and 90°. The sum of the external angles is now seen to be 270° rather than 360°. The argument using parallel lines, as given in question 1 of Problems 1c, is rigorous.

Problems 1c

4. Allow the external angles (in the dynamic argument) to take negative values, or adapt the deduction from the angle sum of a triangle accordingly. There are (surmountable) problems with assuming that such a 'reflex' polygon can always be divided up into a certain number of triangles.

8. 720°.

9. 180°. Use the result of question 7. There is also a nice argument using external angles. How many complete turns would you make in traversing this figure?

10. 360°.

12. 10.

13. 360. Consider external angles — how small could these be?

14. 6.

15. 84°. Think about the irregular pentagon which is 'trapped' in the overlap.

21. $(m, n) = (6, 3)$, $(4, 4)$ or $(3, 6)$. Show that $2(m + n) = mn$, rearrange this in the form $(m - 2)(n - 2) = k$, for some positive integer k, and look for divisors of k.

    Alternatively, consider the two internal angles, which add to 180°. Either both of these are 90°, or one of them is acute. How many possibilities are there?

Chapter 2

As admitted in the Preface, the treatment of congruent triangles is a compromise. It is, in fact, feasible to start with any of the conditions and derive the others. It is also possible to distinguish the two cases ASA and AAS, where the side is either between the two angles or opposite one of them. Moreover, the RHS condition does not, in fact, depend on Pythagoras, as is hinted at in the text. However, the aim of this course is to make students appreciate that the congruence conditions are different and that one must be very careful in applying them. This level of rigour is already beyond the demands of the school curriculum and is, in itself, a worthy achievement. Once this has been mastered, an enthusiastic student can look elsewhere for more formal approaches to the subject. I am grateful to Stuart Simons for the example of the invalid proof of a false result using ASS.

Problems 2a

10. $135°$.

13. $3 : 4 : 6$.

14. $180°$.

15. $48°$.

17. 4.

19. $12 : 4 : 1$.

20. $81°$. Consider the upper edge of the arch. If it were extended, what sort of polygon would be formed?

21. $112.5°$.

Problems 2b

4. Note first that the congruence condition being used is not SAS, but the fallacious ASS. Does this matter? Is the result true despite the mistake in the proof? What type of quadrilateral is $ABCD$?

Problems 2c

4. Consider two cases, where P and Q are on the same and opposite sides of AB.

5. Do not assume that AD bisects $\angle BAC$ without proof.

6. Consider $\triangle BCP$ and $\triangle CBQ$.

8. Once you have found two congruent triangles, consider which rotation would take one of them into the other.

9. Find three congruent triangles.

10. Begin by finding two congruent triangles and then evaluate $\angle XAY$.

11. Draw a line through C parallel to AB, and let X be the point of intersection of this line with C_1B_1. Find two congruent triangles. (Later we will approach this result using similar triangles.)

18. Extend XP to meet AC produced.

19. What assumption is the diagram making? Once you have met the angle bisector theorem, you can view this as a proof that, in a non-isosceles triangle, a median meets the corresponding angle bisector outside the triangle.

Chapter 3

Problems 3a

2. Calculate the area of the triangle in two different ways.

3. 0. Draw diagonals to form a square in the centre.

4. 4.

5. $\frac{1}{4}$. Divide one of the squares into four congruent triangles.

6. $\frac{4}{9}$.

7. 64. Think about the grey and white areas together.

8. 270. Form two simultaneous equations.

9. $\frac{3}{8}$. Divide the hexagon up into small equilateral triangles.

10. 4 : 9. Divide into congruent triangles.

12. 1 : 3.

13. 7 : 24.

14. 40. Divide the hexagon into congruent triangles, using its centre.

15. 1. Divide the shaded area into two isosceles triangles.

16. $\frac{7}{16}$. See question 9 of Problems 2c.

17. 4.

18. 1% decrease.

Problems 3b

1. It is a parallelogram.

2. Add white triangles to both areas.

3. (a) Split $\triangle AEG$ up into three triangles, and use the result of problem 2.

   (b) Look at $\triangle PGQ$, and use the result of problem 2.

4. Look for triangles with the same height.

5. This is *Viviani's theorem*. Join P to each of the vertices of $\triangle ABC$ and calculate areas.

7. Divide $ABCD$ up in different ways and look for triangles of equal area.

8. One approach is to subdivide each of the three quadrilaterals into two triangles by diagonals from the vertices of the original triangle, and then use the ideas of problem 4 (and summation of similar expressions) to derive the relationships $3A = \sum x = 3\sum a.$

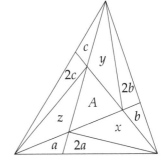

For a discussion of alternative methods, see R J Cook and G V Wood, Feynman's triangle, in *The Mathematical Gazette*, **88** (July 2004).

Chapter 4

Problems 4a

1. This is Euclid's original proof; the configuration is sometimes known as the *Bride's Chair*.

3. This proof is described in *Young Archimedes*, a short story by Aldous Huxley.

5. This proof is associated with US President Garfield.

Problems 4b

1. 30.

2. $\sqrt{2} - 1$.

3. 15. Look for a pair of congruent triangles.

4. $10\sqrt{2} - 1$.

5. 6. Join X to Y and drop a perpendicular from X to the base of the square.

6. $\sqrt{3} - 1$.

7. $\frac{2}{5}$.

8. $8 + 4\sqrt{2}$. Calculate the angles in the star and then subdivide it.

9. You should consider two cases, where D lies between B and C and where D lies outside the segment BC. Does it make any real difference to the proof?

10. Use the converse of Pythagoras' theorem.

13. Use the idea of question 2 of Problems 2d.

Problems 4c

2. Assuming, without loss of generality, that $AB < DC$, drop perpendiculars from A and B to DC.

3. Use the cosine rule on $\triangle ABD$ to find $\cos \angle BDA$ and on $\triangle ADC$ to find $\cos \angle ADC$. How are these related? Otherwise draw the altitude and use Pythagoras' theorem.

5. $3 : 4$.

6. This is *Stewart's theorem*.

7. $\sqrt{3} : 1$. Use the sine rule on $\triangle PQS$ and $\triangle RQS$.

8. $3 : 1$. Let the sides of the black triangle be a, b and c and let the 'new' sides of the grey triangles be a', b' and c'; use the cosine rule (in three different ways) to find relationships between the new and old sides.

Problems 4d

1. It is enough to chase angles and use the fact that $\triangle BC_2C_1$ is isosceles.

2. The smallest value is the perpendicular distance from B to AD and the sine rule degenerates to $\sin A = \frac{a}{c}$. With any smaller value, the arc will fail to meet the ray AD so there will be no triangle.

3. The largest value is when $a = c$ when the point C_1 coincides with A and the sine rule becomes $\sin A = \sin C$, so $\triangle ABC$ is isosceles. With any larger value, the arc meets the ray AD in only one point and $\triangle ABC$ is given uniquely.

4. In terms of the notation in section 2.1, there are two alternative formulations:

   (a) If $\angle CAB = \angle RPQ$ and $AB = PQ$ and $QR = BC > AB$, then $\triangle ABC \equiv \triangle PQR$.

   (b) If $\angle CAB = \angle RPQ > 90°$ and $AB = PQ$ and $QR = BC$, then $\triangle ABC \equiv \triangle PQR$.

Chapter 5

Problems 5a

1. $\frac{24}{49}$. Note that this also follows from question 6 of Problems 3b.

2. 5.

3. $\dfrac{2xy}{(x+y)^2}$.

4. $\frac{2}{5}$.

5. 4.

6. 9.

9. This proof is due to J Barry Sutton, Yet another proof of Pythagoras' theorem, in *The Mathematical Gazette*, **86** (March 2002).

11. $\frac{3}{4}$. Prove that $\triangle ABC$ and $\triangle CBD$ are similar.

Problems 5b

4. It is interesting to reinterpret the figure as a representation of a three-dimensional shape with four faces. The result is still true!

7. $1:4$. First consider $C_1 P$; show that this is parallel to AC, and identify the point where it meets BC. Now do the same for $B_1 Q$.

8. Reflect point A in the bisector of angle B; what can be said about the image?

Problems 5c

3. $1:2$.

4. Find a triangle similar to $\triangle APB$.

7. Construct lines through P and Q parallel to AB.

Chapter 6

Problems 6a

3. Let AP be the perpendicular, and let Q be a point, distinct from P, for which $AQ < AP$.

Problems 6b

2. Draw a diagonal.

4. Draw a diagonal.

5. Let Q be any point on the circle which does not lie on the diameter, join the centre O to Q and use the triangle inequality.

6. The condition for equality is that P is the intersection of AC and BD.

10. One method of showing the right-hand side of the inequality depends on proving that, for instance, $BP + PC < BA + AC$. Do this by producing PC to meet BA at X, and use the triangle inequality twice.

    Alternatively, let the line through P parallel to BC meet AB at S and AC at T, define U, V, W and X in a similar way, and show that

    $$PA + PB + PC < AV + AW + BS + BX + CT + CU < p.$$

Chapter 7

Problems 7a

12. Drop perpendiculars from the centres to PQ and RS. What kind of figure is formed?

13. Again, drop perpendiculars from the centre; what two cases occur?

Problems 7b

6. $75°$.

8. $90°$.

9. 16.

10. 114°.

11. $1 : 2 - \sqrt{3}$. In view of the fact that $\angle XAB = 90°$, what can be said about the point B?

12. Join BD (or AC).

14. Find a point C on the circumference such that $\triangle ABC$ is isosceles.

Problems 7c

3. Begin with the standard diagram showing $\angle AOB$ at the centre of a circle and $\angle ACB$ at the circumference. Are there any other points P such that $\angle APB = \angle AOB$?

4. What can be said about the rectangles $XPVD$ and $UPYB$?

5. Join PO and consider $\angle PAQ$.

6. Find two cyclic quadrilaterals for parts (a) and (b).

10. Prove that $ECDA$ is cyclic.

13. Prove that $EPBA$ is cyclic.

Problems 7d

5. Join CA and DF. As the diagram illustrates, this does not require $ABCDEF$ to be equiangular or equilateral — nor, for instance, is AC parallel to FD.

7. Draw PQ and PZ. I would rate this as the most beautiful simple result about circles.

9. (b) We have the ASS condition, so the triangles are related as in the ambiguous case.

Chapter 8

Problems 8a

3. Two lines parallel to and equidistant from AB.

4. A line parallel to m and midway between A and it.

5. A circle half the radius of C, midway between A and it.

6. A circle concentric with C.

7. The perpendicular bisector of AB.

8. The two angle bisectors.

9. A circle whose diameter is AM, where M is the midpoint of AB.

10. The position of the circumcentre depends on whether the largest angle of the triangle is acute, right or obtuse.

11. A circle with centre at the intersection of m and n and radius $\frac{1}{2}XY$.

12. If QR and ST are parallel, the locus of P is a third parallel line.

   Suppose, then, that QR and ST intersect at X. Let Y be a point on XQR such that $XY = QR$, and similarly let Z be a point on XST such that $XZ = ST$. Then $[PQR] + [PST] = [PXY] + [PXZ] = [XYPZ]$. Hence the locus of X is a straight line parallel to YZ.

8.2 Constructions

It was shown by Mascheroni in 1797 that any Euclidean construction by ruler and compasses could in fact be achieved by compasses alone. To be precise, he showed that any point which can be determined as the intersection of two lines, or as an intersection of a line with a circle, may be achieved by means of circles alone. An account of this can be found by E W Hobson in Chris Pritchard (editor), *The Changing Shape of Geometry*, CUP (2003).

Problems 8b

9. (a) Reflect Y in AB.

   (b) Use the triangle inequality. This is related to Fermat's principle of least time and the reflection of light in a plane mirror.

13. If P is the midpoint of AB, this is easy. If not, let P be nearer B than A. Join P to B_1, the midpoint of AC; then let the line through B parallel to PB_1 cut AC at Q. Then PQ is the desired line.

14. Join AC.

15. If all else fails, you can use coordinate geometry here. Then try to prove it otherwise.

16. As 15.

Chapter 9

Problems 9a

7. Draw a circle on diameter OP.

Problems 9b

1. $\sqrt{2} - 1$.

2. $90° - \frac{1}{2}x$.

3. 2.

4. 4.

5. 5.

6. $3 + 2\sqrt{2}$. Mark the centre of the circle and calculate various lengths, using Pythagoras' theorem.

7. $\dfrac{\pi\sqrt{2}}{2}$. Form the triangle of centres.

8. 6. Join all four centres and use Pythagoras' theorem.

10. $\sqrt{5} + 1 : 1$.

11. $2\sqrt{st}$. Draw the triangle formed by the centres, making use of the result, in question 3 of Problems 9a, that the line of centres passes through the point of tangency. Drop perpendiculars from the centres to the two parallel lines, and more perpendiculars to form right-angled triangles. Then use Pythagoras' theorem and some algebra.

12. Two angle bisectors.

14. Join OE.

15. Join OE.

18. First show that there is a circle tangential to AB, BC and CD. Suppose this is not tangential to AD. There are two cases, according to whether AD cuts the circle or not. Draw a tangent from A to the circle, meeting DC at D', and derive a contradiction concerning $\triangle ADD'$.

20. This, and other so-called 'eyeball theorems', are discussed by Antonio Gutierrez in Chris Pritchard (editor), *The Changing Shape of Geometry*, CUP (2003).

21. $\dfrac{\sqrt{5}+1}{2}$: 1, the *golden ratio* (see question 7 of Problems 10d).

Problems 9c

3. $90° - a - \frac{1}{2}(b+c)$. Join ST and use the alternate segment theorem twice.

4. $3\theta - 180°$.

5. Draw the common tangent. Note that there are two possible diagrams.

11. Join PQ.

14. Join BC and BD. Find the tangent to one circumcircle and show it is also tangent to the other one.

Problems 9d

1. If the distance between the centres is a, then the two answers are $\sqrt{a^2 - d^2}$ and $\sqrt{a^2 - s^2}$.

2. Draw the tangent at A.

5. Join PQ.

Chapter 10

Problems 10a

2. $\dfrac{4 - \pi}{4}$.

3. $2 + \pi$.

4. 64. Notice that in this question, as elsewhere in this set of problems, we have a shape with curved sides whose area is independent of π.

5. $\frac{1}{2}$.

6. $2\pi - 2$.

7. $5 : 7$.

8. $\frac{3}{4}$.

9. $7 : 2$.

10. This idea is due to Mamikon Mnatsakanian, and generalises to give a method for calculating areas without using any calculus.

11. 2. Inscribe a square on diameter AB.

12. 2. It is actually possible to get the answer without calculating specific areas involving π. The four semicircles have a total area equal to the white circle. It is then easy to show that the shaded area is equal to that of the square.

13. $23 - 16\sqrt{2}$.

14. π. Use the symmetry of the figure and join the vertices of the equilateral triangle to the centre of the big circle.

15. $\frac{\pi(2+\sqrt{2})}{2} - 2\sqrt{2}$. Draw several radii from O, the centre of the circle.

16. The three different areas that occur are given by

$$2 - \sqrt{2}, \quad \frac{\pi}{8} + \frac{3\sqrt{2}}{4} - 1 \quad \text{and} \quad \frac{\pi}{8} + \frac{1}{2} - \frac{\sqrt{2}}{2}.$$

I am grateful to Nick Lord for this question.

17. $\frac{3\sqrt{3}}{2}$. For this area, see J V Narlikar, A pi-less area, in *The Mathematical Gazette*, **65** (March 1981).

Problems 10b

2. This result leads to a construction for a line segment which is the geometric mean of two other segments.

5. Consider the midpoint of AX.

8. Use the rectangle property once and then the tangent-secant theorem twice.

11. This is an interpretation of the cosine rule.

12. The proof requires some delicacy. Let O be the intersection of AB and CD, and write down the rectangle property. Now let EO meet circle C_1 at F_1 and circle C_3 at F_3. Argue that F_1 and F_3 are the same point and identify it.

13. Let P lie on the line AB (but not between A and B). Then the tangent-secant theorem guarantees that the tangents are equal. You must then argue that if P is to the side of this line, the tangents are not equal.

14. First establish that CQ is a tangent to the circumcircle of $\triangle AEQ$, with a similar result for CP.

15. This is a proof of a famous inequality relating the harmonic, geometric and arithmetic means, together with the root-mean-square, of two positive numbers. I am grateful to Nick Lord for suggesting it.

Problems 10c

3. For a fixed position of C, the point P lies on the circle with diameter BC. Hence $\angle APC = 90°$ and the locus is the circle on diameter AB.

4. What can be said about the circumcircle of $\triangle AXY$ in relation to AT?

Problems 10d

3. Apply Ptolemy to $AYDX$ and use similar triangles.

Problems 10e

5. For a fixed ratio λ, the point P lies on an Apollonius circle with centre O; clearly this circle intersects the line ℓ. As λ increases, what happens to the radius of the circle? Which circle will correspond to the largest possible value of λ? What is its radius? Show that the maximum value of λ satisfies the equation $\lambda^2 - \lambda - 1 = 0$. Note the re-appearance of the golden ratio.

Chapter 11

The circumcentre has already appeared in question 10 of Problems 8a, the orthocentre in question 6 of Problems 7c and the incentre (and excentres) in questions 8 and 9 of Problems 9a.

Problems 11a

2. Use the sine rule to calculate the distance AP.

4. Let L, M and N be the midpoints of AD, BD and CD; what can be said about these three points and about the quadrilateral $LZND$?

7. Consider the quadrilateral O_1XO_2Y.

12. What can be said about the quadrilateral $BCEF$? What is the significance of A_1 in this respect?

13. Let QN be the altitude from Q to AB and let H be the orthocentre of $\triangle ABQ$; prove that $\frac{QH}{QN}$ is a constant k. Let P' be the point on QP

such that $\frac{QP'}{QP} = k$, and show that H lies on a circle with diameter $P'Q$.

15. (d) One way of proving this is to think of the triangle as made up of thin strips parallel to the side AB. The centre of mass of each strip is at the midpoint, so the centre of mass of the whole triangle lies on the median through A. A similar argument applies to the other two medians. (Note that this is an alternative proof of the concurrency of the medians.)

17. This is a difficult problem. It is possible to prove it by using the sine rule, or by appealing to some more sophisticated geometrical results. An approach using similar triangles can be found in the UKMT yearbook for 2005-2006. Alternatively, here is a proof which needs only the circle theorems.

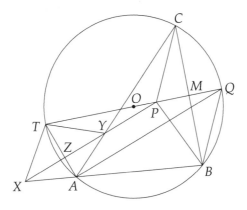

Draw the circumcircle of $\triangle ABC$ and the internal bisector of $\triangle CAB$, meeting the circle at Q. Since arc $BQ =$ arc CQ, the point Q lies on the diameter through M, the midpoint of BC, and P also lies on this diameter. Note also that AQ is parallel to XP, since $\triangle XAY$ is isosceles and so $\angle QAB = \frac{1}{2}\angle CAB = \angle PXB$.

Let T be the other end of the diameter QO. Now $\angle TCA = \angle TBA$, $TC = TB$ and $CA = BX$, so $\triangle TCA \equiv \triangle TBX$ (SAS), and hence $TA = TX$.

Now $\angle TPX = \angle TQA = \angle TBA = \angle TBX$ so $TPBX$ is cyclic. Hence $\angle MPB = \angle TXA = \angle TAX = \angle TQB$ (cyclic quadrilaterals). But now $\angle CPB = \angle CQB = 180° - \angle CAB$ as required.

Problems 11b

5. One way of solving this problem is to break it into parts.
   (a) Prove $AE = C_1A$ and hence that $\triangle OC_1A \equiv \triangle HEA$.
   (b) Prove that $\triangle OC_1P \equiv \triangle HEQ$ and deduce the result.

6. First prove that P is the orthocentre of $\triangle LMN$; this establishes the collinearity of three of the points. Now focus on $\triangle ABC$, and prove that P is its circumcentre and S its orthocentre. Now we have another Euler line and can show that the four points are equally spaced along a line.

Problems 11c

3. If the two nine-point circles are to touch, where must the point of contact be? Use the alternate segment theorem to establish the direction of the two tangents at this point, and show that they coincide.

4. Use the alternate segment theorem to find the direction of the tangent.

Problems 11d

3. This argument is due to Jack Oliver, Pythagoras' theorem: an alternative to Note 79.57, in *The Mathematical Gazette*, **91** (March 1997).

5. Use the result of question 1(a).

6. Use the result of question 16 of Problems 9b.

8. Focus on $\triangle PQR$. By considering the lengths QD, DY, YE and ER, and using the alternate segment theorem, prove something about the lines PY and QR.

9. What is the relationship between the point Q and $\triangle ABP$?

10. Consider the orthic triangle $\triangle DEF$ and use the result of question 2(b) of Problems 11b.

   Alternatively, use angles in the same segment: $\angle ADZ = \angle ACZ = 90° - \angle A$ and $\angle ADY = \angle ABY = 90° - \angle A$, and so AD bisects $\angle ZXY$.

11. Think about $\triangle AQR$: what is the significance of P? This tells you something about PR, and then a simple angle chase does the trick. For some alternative methods, look in the UKMT yearbook for 2000–2001, page 111.

Problems 11e

3. Note that this shows that the existence of the orthocentre follows from the existence of the circumcentre.

4. The excentres are A, B and C.

8. From the viewpoint of the excentral triangle, what is the circumcircle of $\triangle ABC$?

9. Again, view this geometrical fact from the standpoint of the excentral triangle, and see if it is a known property of triangles.

11.5   The Simson line

The Simson line is also referred to as the *Wallace-Simson line*, since the theorem was actually discovered, in 1799, by the Scottish mathematician William Wallace.

Problems 11f

4. In part (b), argue by reference to the arcs PC and $N'F'$, and in (c), use the fact that $HF = FF'$ established earlier.

8. Use the result of problem 7 to show that the Simson lines are perpendicular. Now show that the midpoints of HP and HQ are at either end of a diameter of the nine-point circle, and then deduce that the Simson lines meet on this circle. In fact, the nine-point circle could be thought of as the locus of the intersection as P varies.

Problems 11g

3. Use the trapezium $OHDA_1$ and Pythagoras' theorem, and calculate various useful results by trigonometry.

Chapter 12

Problems 12a

7. Show that H is the centre of similitude of the nine-point circle and the circumcircle.

8. Extend XY to meet C_2 again at Z. It is sufficient to show that O_1X is parallel to O_2Z.

Problems 12b

5. Use the sine rule to find the ratios in which BY cuts AC, etc. Alternatively, prove that $\triangle ABY \equiv \triangle AZC$ and show that the angle between BY and CZ is 120°, without using Ceva's theorem. The intersection is also the common point of the circumcentres of the equilateral triangles.

   The Fermat point is the solution to *Torricelli's problem*, that of finding a point X such that $AX + BX + CX$ is minimised. It is worth asking what happens when $\triangle ABC$ is not acute-angled.

8. Use areas.

9. Again think about areas.

   Another pretty theorem of van Aubel which you might like to prove is that if P, Q, R and S are the centres of squares erected externally on the sides of quadrilateral $ABCD$, then PR and QS have the same length and are perpendicular to each other.

Problems 12d

1. Use the angle bisector theorem. This argument also shows the ratios in which the incentre divides the angle bisectors.

4. This turns out to be the Nagel point of $\triangle ABC$, as defined in question 5 of Problems 12a.

Chapter 13

The quotation on page 131 comes from Geoff Smith, in *A Mathematical Olympiad Primer*, UKMT, 2008.

Problems 13a

7. If P and Q are parallel, PQ passes through the centre of inversion, and its pole is the 'line at infinity'.

9. Identify the poles of AP, BQ and CR with respect to the incircle and use the facts (question 4 of Problems 12b, question 3 of Problems 12d) that these three lines are concurrent.

   Alternatively, use Ceva's theorem. The line through X, Y and Z is called the *Gergonne line*.

Problems 13c

7. As well as the circle of inversion Γ, any circle orthogonal to Γ inverts to itself. These are the only circles which have this property.

Problems 13d

The diagrams below show the inverses of the configurations described in the problems. Parts of the diagram shown in *grey* are objects in the *original* configuration. The centre of inversion O (which does not exist in the image under inversion) is also indicated. A point labelled as A is the inverse image of the point which was called A in the original configuration.

1. Invert the three circles in O. The images of A, B and C form a triangle, with AO perpendicular to BC and BO perpendicular to AC. Why? Remember question 2 of Problems 13c.

   What is the point O in relation to $\triangle ABC$?

   How does this prove the desired result?

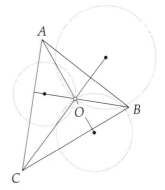

2. Invert in O. The circles become straight lines AC and BD, and the tangents become circles through O tangential to AC at A and C and to CD at C and D. The circumcircles of $\triangle OAB$ and $\triangle OCD$ become lines AB and CD.

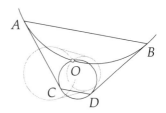

What must be proved about these lines and why is it true?

3. Invert in O. The circle $OABC$ becomes the line ABC, and the lines AB and BC become circles intersecting at O and B.

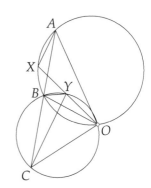

The images of X and Y are collinear with O, and the circles OAX and OCY become lines AX and BY. What must be proved about them?

4. Invert in O. The line becomes a circle and A, B and C points on it. Any circle through O becomes a line — but what happens to its centre? So where are the points X, Y and Z?

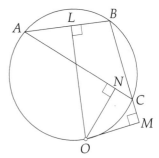

It is worth considering the points L, M and N in the diagram. What must be proved about these points?

5. Invert in P and let P' be the other point of intersection of the orthogonal circles. These become perpendicular lines through the image of P', and the circle XQR becomes a circle tangential to these lines. The circles XPQ and XPR become lines XQ and XR, and we must prove that $\angle QXR = 45°$.

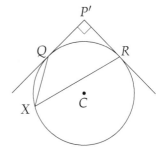

6. Invert in A. The two circles through A' become perpendicular lines through the image of A', and the third circle becomes a circle cutting both lines at right angles. The circumcircles become the lines BC and $C'B'$. We must prove something about these two lines.

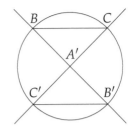

7. Invert in the circumcircle. The points A, B, C and D do not move, but the circles OAB, OBC, OCD and ODA become lines. The images of the circumcentres are as in problem 4.

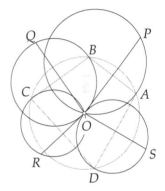

   The lines PB and QB become circles OPB and OQB; where are their centres? Now $\angle PBQ$ is the angle between these circles; can we identify this?

8. Invert the circles through O to two parallel straight lines $\mathcal{C}_1$ and $\mathcal{C}_2$. The line AB inverts to another line. The tangents invert to two circles $\mathcal{T}_1$ and $\mathcal{T}_2$ tangential to $\mathcal{C}_1$ and $\mathcal{C}_2$ which meet on AB. We need to show that the circles $\mathcal{T}_1$ and $\mathcal{T}_2$ touch.

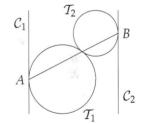

   Note that, by inverting, we have changed the result to its converse.

Problems 13e

1. See question 1 of Problems 11d.

2. See question 7 of Problems 13c. The incircle inverts to itself.

6. See question 11 of Problems 13b. Then use question 7 of Problems 13b to show that the image is X.

7. See question 2 of Problems 13c and question 4 of Problems 11c.

9. BC is one of the transverse common tangents to the incircle and excircle, and AX is the line of centres of these two circles.

10. Inversion preserves angles, and hence tangency.

Sources of the problems

The following tables show the original provenance of problems which have appeared in competitions administered by the UKMT. The symbols J, I and S stand for the Junior, Intermediate and Senior Mathematical Challenges, and B1 and B2 stand for the two stages of the British Mathematical Olympiad.

Problems 1c

6.	J	1999	13
7.	J	2006	7
8.	I	2004	4
9.	S	2005	13
10.	I	2005	7
12.	S	1999	7
13.	I	2003	15
15.	I	2006	19

Problems 2a

6.	J	2005	13
7.	J	2002	21
8.	J	2003	23
9.	J	2005	23
10.	I	1997	11
11.	I	1999	8
12.	I	2002	16
13.	I	1998	19
14.	I	2005	13

15.	J	2004	20
17.	I	2003	8
19.	I	2005	25
20.	I	2005	14
21.	S	1998	12

Problems 3a

3.	I	1998	24
4.	I	2005	18
5.	J	2001	9
6.	S	2005	4
7.	J	2001	25
8.	J	2004	24
9.	J	2006	16
10.	I	2001	8
11.	I	2003	19
12.	I	2004	21
13.	S	2000	5
14.	S	2001	8
15.	S	2001	12
16.	S	2003	21

17.	S	1999	13
18.	S	2000	13

Problems 3b

7.	B1	2006	2

Problems 4b

1.	I	1997	20
2.	I	1999	25
3.	S	2004	8
4.	I	2003	24
5.	S	2003	17
6.	S	2001	14
7.	I	2006	24
8.	S	2005	17

Problems 4c

6.	S	2004	21
7.	S	2001	25

Problems 5a

1.	I	1998	25
2.	S	2003	12
3.	I	2002	18
4.	I	2004	25
5.	I	2006	23
6.	S	2004	22
11.	S	1997	15

Problems 5c

3.	I	2004	18

Problems 7b

6.	I	2000	8
7.	I	2003	22
8.	S	2000	19
9.	S	1998	12
10.	S	2003	20
11.	S	2002	23
13.	B1	2002	2

Problems 7c

11.	B1	2004	2

Problems 7d

8.	B1	2006	3

Problems 9b

1.	S	2000	21
2.	S	2001	20
3.	S	2003	24
4.	I	2005	21
5.	S	2004	16
6.	S	1998	23
7.	S	2002	16
8.	S	2004	24
10.	S	2001	23
11.	S	2000	25

Problems 9c

3.	S	2002	21
4.	S	2004	18

Problems 9d

6.	B1	2000	1
7.	B1	2007	4

Problems 10a

2.	I	1997	17
3.	I	2003	17
4.	I	2004	12
5.	I	1999	13
6.	I	2006	21

7.	S	2002	11
8.	S	1998	4
9.	S	2004	10
11.	I	2001	25
12.	I	1997	23
13.	S	1999	22
14.	S	2005	23
15.	S	1998	25

Problems 10b

8.	B2	2004	1
9.	B2	2000	1
14.	B1	2005	2

Problems 11a

8.	B1	2003	2
16.	B2	2006	3

Problems 11b

5.	B2	2007	3

Problems 11d

8.	B2	1999	2
9.	B2	2005	2
11.	B2	2001	3

In addition, the following problems have been taken from textbooks.
Problems 2c, question 17: Durell, *A New Geometry for Schools*.

Problems 7c, question 4 and Problems 9c, question 9: Godfrey and Siddons, *A Shorter Geometry*.

Problems 7c, question 8: Hall and Stevens, *A School Geometry*.

Ideas for further reading

Books currently in print

Nathan Altshiller-Court, *College Geometry*. Dover, 2007.
  This is a modern reprint of an excellent textbook from 1952, which uses an interesting approach stressing construction problems.

C J Bradley, *The Algebra of Geometry*. HighPerception, 2007.
  This book explores advanced geometry from an algebraic viewpoint, including cartesian, areal and projective methods.

C J Bradley, *Challenges in Geometry*. Oxford University Press, 2004.
  This book uses number theory to solve problems in Euclidean geometry involving integers and rational numbers.

H S M Coxeter and Samuel L Greitzer, *Geometry Revisited*. New Mathematical Library, MAA, 1996.
  This reprint of a classic text from 1967 explores modern approaches to the subject, including transformations, inversion and projective methods.

A D Gardiner and C J Bradley, *Plane Euclidean Geometry: Theory and Problems*. UKMT, 2005.
  This handbook for young mathematicians develops Euclidean geometry in a fairly formal way as well as introducing areal coordinates and approaches using vectors and complex numbers.

Ross Honsberger, *Episodes in Nineteenth and Twentieth Century Euclidean Geometry*. New Mathematical Library, MAA, 1995.
  This wonderful book revels in unexpected and beautiful results, using only synthetic methods.

Roger A Johnson, *Advanced Euclidean Geometry*. Dover, 2007.

This is a welcome reprint of a standard text, first published in 1929, covering all aspects of triangle and circle geometry.

Alfred Posamentier, *Advanced Euclidean Geometry*.

Despite the title, this is not particularly advanced; it includes a CD-ROM with interactive sketches using GSP.

Alfred S Posamentier and Charles T Salkind, *Challenging Problems in Geometry*. Dover, 1988.

This is a stimulating collection of problems, arranged by topic and in order of difficulty.

Chris Pritchard (ed), *The Changing Shape of Geometry*. Cambridge University Press, 2003.

This collection of short essays covers a wide range of geometrical topics and applications.

John Silvester, *Geometry Ancient and Modern*. Oxford University Press, 2001.

This undergraduate teaching text relates geometry to ideas from algebra, complex numbers, transformations and group theory.

David Wells, *The Penguin Dictionary of Curious and Interesting Geometry*. Penguin, 1991.

This is a book to dip into, a collection of geometrical gems.

Available at the library

H S M Coxeter, *Introduction to Geometry*. John Wiley, 1961.

This is a demanding but rewarding overview of the subject, with material on three dimensional geometry, non-Euclidean geometry, geometry of curves and topology.

C V Durell, *Modern Geometry*. Macmillan, 1919.

This excellent school textbook was in use as late as the 1960s.

E A Maxwell, *Geometry for Advanced Pupils*. Oxford University Press, 1949.

This stimulating approach proceeds by examining various configurations and mining them for all the nuggets they can furnish.

Websites

The web is a notoriously fickle place, with sites tending to appear and disappear without warning. The list below contains three which are each, in their own way, a labour of love.

http://mathworld.wolfram.com/

This is an invaluable resource, being an encyclopaedia of mathematics, extensively cross-referenced, and, remarkably, the creation of one man, Eric Weisstein.

http://faculty.evansville.edu/ck6/encyclopedia/ETC.html

Created and maintained by Clark Kimberling, this 'encyclopaedia of triangle centres' currently lists some 600 points associated with the triangle, including over 100 on the Euler line.

http://www.math.fau.edu/yiu/geometry.html

This is Paul Yiu's website; it contains a cornucopia of geometrical problems, lecture notes and interactive demonstrations.

Software

There are now a number of 'interactive' programs available, which enable you to explore geometry dynamically by moving points around and seeing what properties of the diagram remain invariant. Amongst the most popular applications are *Cabri*, *The Geometer's Sketchpad*, *Geometry Expressions*, *Geocadabra* and *GeoGebra*. Some of these enable you to work in three (or more) dimensions and to carry out calculations in symbolic algebra.